BILL HARVEY'S
60 YEARS IN STEAM

D.W. Harvey

DAVID & CHARLES
Newton Abbot   London   North Pomfret (Vt)

Associated Society of
Locomotive Engineers & Firemen

A. E. GRIFFITHS, General Secretary

NORWICH BRANCH
Mr.D.W.Harvey
Depot Manager
Norwich.

Branch Secretary:
G. GRIGGLESTONE,
30 Lincoln Street,
Norwich.
NOR 51F.
17th September 1970

Dear Sir,
    On behalf of the Norwich Branch of this society, I
feel it's only right and proper,that I convey to you,our thoughts and
feelings at this moment in time,regarding your pending retirement.
    The 25 years you have been at Norwich,have been very
happy years,so far as the relationship between Management and Men have
been concerned.We think with pleasure the very real and deep under -
standing you have always had for your fellow man.
    You Sir,have always been to us all,much more than just
a figure head,never hesitating to show compassion and feeling when ever
you thought these were the dispositions proper to man.This to us Loco -
Men has not gone by unnoticed,even if we have not perhaps,always shown,
by word or deed,the high esteem with which we hold you.
    Sir,you to us,are the last of real Loco - Men.My wish
is that you may draw some comfort in the knowledge,that when ever Loco -
Men congregate and talk "Bill Harvey".will always be mentioned with
a great deal of affection.
    We wish you good health,good luck,and a long
and happy retirement.

For and on behalf of the Norwich Motive Power Dept.
    I am yours sincerely
    Branch Secretary

British Library Cataloguing in Publication Data

Harvey, D. W.
    Bill Harvey's sixty years in steam.
    1. Harvey, D. W.   2. Railways – Great
    Britain – Employees – Biography
    3. Locomotives – Great Britain
    I. Title
    625.2′61′0924   TJ603.5.H32/

    ISBN 0–7153–8712–X

Photoset in Linotron Plantin by
Northern Phototypesetting Co, Bolton
and printed in Great Britain
by Redwood Burn Limited, Trowbridge, Wilts
for David & Charles Publishers plc
Brunel House Newton Abbot Devon

Published in the United States of America
by David & Charles Inc
North Pomfret Vermont 05053 USA

CONTENTS

AUTHOR'S NOTE

Few day-to-day records of the steam age on the railways survive, and those that do need adequate interpretation if they are to be of any historical value – this I have endeavoured to do.

The technical content forms the most important part of this locomotive history. It covers data recording in detail, the extent and cost of repairs necessary to keep certain classes of steam locomotives running, together with copies of drawings and official reports which led to alterations in design and so on. This is a descriptive history, which it is hoped will appeal to the general reader, supplemented with historic and technical data for the serious student.

I am indebted to the following for permission to reproduce extracts from various records: the Council of the Institution of Mechanical Engineers for extracts from the *Journal* of the Institution of Locomotive Engineers, No 197, *The Railway Gazette* for a summary of results of the 1948 locomotive interchange trials. Also to the following for permission to reproduce photographs Dr I. C. Allen, J. Aylard, J. V. Bramwell, British Railways Board, Cusworth Hall Museum, Doncaster, Eastern Daily Press, K. H. Leech, Locomotive Publishing Company (Ian Allen) and the Castle Museum, Norwich.

My thanks are due to Mrs M. Ritchie for typing the orignal manuscript. The encouragement for the commencement of my authorship came from a number of colleagues to whom I paid tribute in my first book.

The final realisation is mainly due to the skill and support of Mrs Eileen da Silva, a good editor and a good friend.

D. W. Harvey, Norwich

FOREWORD

Many books have been written about the design and the designers of steam locomotives and about their successes, failures and performance. This book is not one of them; it is, in fact, an autobiographical account of the life's work of one man concerned with the maintenance of steam railway engines, a task that was as unglamorous as it was important to the railways in seeking to achieve the highest standard of safety, reliability and economy in service.

From the day his engineering apprenticeship began in the Doncaster Locomotive Works of the Great Northern Railway, D. W. Harvey strove to acquire every scrap of knowledge he possibly could, not only about the engines upon which he worked but also about the principles and practice of mechanical engineering which was his calling. Throughout his career he stored that knowledge in a memory of exceptional capacity but also recorded almost every fact in minute detail in capacious notebooks generously illustrated with freehand sketches.

The work described by the author covered some 46 years – and more since his retirement – which, included periods of extraordinary difficulty readily identifiable in the narrative. The first embraced the years of depression after the first world war when the grouping of the railways into the four main-line companies encountered financial stringency which curtailed expenditure to an extent that made adequate maintenance almost impossible.

The steady acceleration of passenger services that took place in the years before the outbreak of war in 1939 was immediately followed by the enormous increase in traffic for the conveyance of men and materials which lasted throughout the war years. This again produced arrears of maintenance work that it took years to recover when peace returned. The author bore more than a fair share of responsibility for the gradual but successful outcome of these years of strenuous endeavour.

Steam traction lasted through the first twenty years of Nationalisation of British Railways and in that period reached the zenith of its performance but even then the maintenance engineer's lot did not become an easy one because there were all too many instances in which the demands made on the engines were not matched by the quality of the equipment provided. It was in these circumstances that Bill Harvey was called upon, as he had been several times during his career, to come to the rescue of a depot which was seriously failing to meet the demands made upon it. In this instance the design of new engines provided for the exacting commuter service was entirely unsuitable. The indictment implied in the author's description of this state of affairs is amply justified.

Bill's reward for the way in which he met this challenge came with his return to his own depot at Norwich from which the BR Standard Britannia class engines were a few months later working an accelerated passenger service with a sparkling degree of success which brought a contented smile to the face of our author who, in other circumstances, was not always given to smiling!

In this short foreword I make no apology for having written about Bill Harvey, a colleague since our Doncaster days. His book, at once a detailed account of his life's work and, at the same time a fascinating treatise on the technical features of maintenance of the steam locomotive in the last five decades of its existence, speaks for itself. It is too, I believe, quite unique in that it fills a gap in history concerning the work that was done behind the scenes and in conditions in the depots that could only be described as ranging from horribly uncomfortable to absolutely appalling. That D.W.H. never failed to earn the respect and admiration of his men as well as their gratitude for all he taught them is a tribute to the born leader that he was.

T. C. B. Miller
Chief Mechanical and Electrical Engineer
British Railways Board Headquarters (1968–71)

CHAPTER 1
TOP TURNERY

There was no doubt in my mind as to what I wanted to do when I left school – to become a steam locomotive engineer! But how to achieve this ambition perplexed my parents, and after considering several possibilities it was decided that I should be entered as an artificer or engineering apprentice at the then newly-opened RAF establishment at Cranwell in Lincolnshire.

In all probability that is where I would have gone but for a chance remark to my father from a service colleague, that he had a son who was a premium apprentice of Mr H. N. Gresley at the Great Northern Railway locomotive works at Doncaster. (That son, Bernard Cyril Symes subsequently became Chief Locomotive Draughtsman at Doncaster and a lifelong friend.)

My father lost no time in writing to Mr Gresley, the Chief Mechanical Engineer of the LNER. This was followed by a meeting at King's Cross with his personal assistant, O. V. S. Bulleid, which resulted in my being summoned to Doncaster on 28 December 1923 for an interview with Francis Wintour, the Assistant Mechanical Engineer for the Southern Area of the newly-formed London & North Eastern Railway.

I remember vividly the journey north behind an Ivatt large Atlantic, the sound of its sharp staccato exhaust and the patter of cinders descending on the elliptical roof of the open saloon coach in which I rode, as blowing-off at the safety valves it climbed the snow-clad Lincolnshire wolds sparkling in the sunshine to the summit at Stoke, and a fleeting glimpse at Grantham, of small Atlantic No 3983 the only 'Klondyke' to have an outside-frame bogie.

My interview with Mr Wintour was brief but satisfactory, and I was bidden to report for duty in ten days' time at 8.00 am, ready to start work.

On Monday 7 January 1924 my father (who had come to see me safely installed in suitable lodgings) and I were ushered into the Works Manager's Office at the Doncaster plant, a lofty spacious

apartment furnished solidly in Victorian style and adorned with
large framed photographs of GNR locomotives mostly of H. A.
Ivatt's design, and heated by a blazing open fire replenished at
intervals by a uniformed attendant.

We were received kindly by F. H. Eggleshaw, the Works
Manager, a tall, thoughtful-looking man with a slight cough, who
had made his name during World War I, when in charge of the
Forge, by considerably extending and improving the range of
articles produced by the drop-forging process. Mr Eggleshaw
outlined briefly the five year course of training that I would
receive, and then provided us with a guide to look round the
Works. After lunch at the nearby YMCA where I was to lodge I
donned my overalls for the first time and reported for work to Billy
Carr, at his marking-off table in the Top Turnery, the traditional
starting point for all new premium apprentices.

The long vista of overhead shafting and counter shafts with a
forest of belts driving the machines below and the hum these
produced was impressive in the extreme, creating as it did an
impression of intense activity missing from a modern machine
shop with an independent motor drive to each machine.

As the sun was setting, I saw from the turnery window the
4.11pm train hauled by a Gresley Pacific leave for London bearing
my father with it. It was then as Wilmott the beltman turned on
the yellow gas lights one by one, that I experienced a sharp but
fortunately brief attack of home-sickness. This was soon forgotten
amid the helter-skelter of hundreds of feet hurrying across the
plant footbridge as the smiths' shop buzzer blew 5.30pm, and the
prospect of making new friends among the thirteen other
premiums then resident in the YMCA.

The following morning as dawn was breaking, I joined the
crowd of overalled workmen converging on the plant footbridge,
and remember being jostled by those hurrying to more distant
parts of the works, anxious not 'to lose a quarter', the penalty for
being late.

On crossing the footbridge, a door on the left facing the
gatehouse led into the Top Turnery. On opening this door the
senses were immediately assailed by the rattle of bars in the
Gridley automatic bolt-making machines and the pungent smell of
hot lard oil used as a cutting fluid.

The machines in this section (known as the Monkeys' Cage)
were tended by small, cheeky urchins attired in oilcloth aprons

with sleeved forearms. Beyond the cage came the relative calm of the machine shop proper with its batteries of lathes, milling, drilling, slotting and shaping machines and last of all, separated from the main body of the shop by a screen, the brass finishing shop, presided over by William Corbett, a local councillor, whose brother George sometimes embarrassed him by being fined for being found on licensed premises after 6 o'clock in the evening when off sick. Fitters' benches lined the walls under the windows overlooking the south end of the station and the view from these was of unfailing interest, as trains from four other companies beside the Great Northern served Doncaster.

After clocking-on I reported to Billy Carr, a quiet, tobacco-chewing, highly-skilled mechanic, who instructed me in the art of translating from a blueprint the various centre lines and circles to guide the machinist onto the numerous rough forgings and castings neatly stacked round the massive cast-iron marking-off table. First these were given a coat of lime wash and dried at a nearby gas-fired hotplate (a great comfort in those days as the turnery was unheated) in order that the lines scribed on them should show up clearly. Next the article to be marked-off was placed on the plane surface of the table and levelled with wedges and a square. A centre line was then scribed round it with a scribling block and from this datum all centres and arcs of circles shown on the drawing were made and centre-popped. Sometimes the forging was a bit scant in one dimension and full in another and the art was to so position the datum line that the best possible use was made of the material. The marking-off table was as good a position as any from which to survey the conditions prevailing at that time in railway workshops.

In 1924 the eight-hour day had been in existence for less than five years, and another seventeen were to elapse before railway shopmen received paid holidays. Many of the amenities taken for granted today were not yet even thought of. There were no general washing facilities, canteens, or clothes lockers – men came to and from work in their greasy overalls and hung their outer clothing on nails over their benches or machines.

Time-keeping was strict and punctuality the rule; occasional latecomers were allowed to 'lose a quarter;' persistent latecomers were sent home at the discretion of the foremen, who stood by the clocks and saw the card boxes locked as soon as the buzzer blew. These latecomers would lose half-a-day's pay.

As piecework was the general rule and earnings depended on it, no undue delay occurred in starting work, which continued steadily until a few minutes before finishing time. The foremen spent most of their time in the shop supervising and urging the flow of work from one section to another, and very little in the office.

The day's output was recorded with a pencil stump onto a whitewashed wooden tablet, for transfer later to the piecework voucher. These tablets were also used for making crude dimensional sketches of details extracted from the shop's drawing on canvas-backed cartridge paper attached to a stick like a flag, as newspapers are in some Continental countries.

The unheated gas-lit turneries built by Archibald Sturrock in 1853 and still to be seen facing Doncaster Station, were manned largely by boy apprentices, middle-aged chargemen and elderly men, many still wearing the mechanics' old traditional dress of corduroy trousers, white canvas jacket, red-spotted neckerchief and a home-made American style cap of black sateen. It was a sight to be remembered to see these grave men with their lined, seamed, faces gather round for the Monday morning distribution of snuff from the snuff club. Smoking anywhere in the works or offices was strictly forbidden – consequently snuff taking and tobacco chewing were common, as evidenced by the foul breath and yellow teeth of those addicted to the habit, who were expert at ejecting a thin stream of nicotine-stained saliva with considerable accuracy. I was tempted once to try chewing thin black twist, but never again! It took hours and several visits to the smithy water tap to get rid of the vile, scorching taste of the tobacco.

Although unheated the turnery was quite comfortable to work in due to the heat generated by the cutting tools removing metal. A characteristic of the turnery was the smell of phenol, a strong carbolic disinfectant fluid sprayed from a watering can by Arthur Boulby the bandy-legged shop labourer. Phenol was also used as an inexpensive cutting fluid and coolant by turners and machinists, hence the all-pervading smell.

Sanitation consisted of open trough latrines. Those at the Crimpsall had half-doors on which a superannuated attendant knocked when he thought the occupant had sat there long enough. This construction provided the more mischievous apprentices with a wonderful opportunity of disturbing their elders communing with nature and enjoying a surreptitious smoke, by igniting a ball of newspaper at the 'upstream' end. Drake's fireships amongst the Spanish Armada was as nothing to the commotion caused by this diversion!

The ordinary apprentices who started work at fourteen years of age in order to contribute to the family income, had the advantage over the premiums and pupils of two years' experience in the works, and were in consequence much more mature in their ways and outlook. This disparity soon disappeared, for whereas the ordinary apprentices were generally local boys living at home, the premiums and pupils mostly came from 'away' (two even from India) and therefore lived in digs or lodgings where they quickly learned self-reliance and independence. For them, there was no raiding the family store for items like matches or shoe polish. Such items as the cost of laundering overalls had to come out of the apprentices' wages, together with a contribution towards their keep. At sixteen this was 16s 8d (£0.83p) per week, at seventeen 17s 3d (£0.86p), and at eighteen 18s 9d (£0.94p). At nineteen years of age they were expected to be self-supporting with the exception of clothes. Digs then as now varied both in price and quality. Often the cheapest were among the best especially when one lived with the family; these could cost from £1 5s 0d (£1.25p) to £1 15s 0d (£1.75p). Digs with a private room in the Hall Gate and Christchurch Road area could cost £2.50p or perhaps more. When engaging digs it was important to enquire whether the rooms could be retained during the Race (St Leger) Week; many landladies made a useful addition to their income by letting lodgings to racegoers. Indeed whole houses in Regent Square, where H. A. Ivatt once lived, were let for as much as £40 a week, a great deal of money in those days.

The works was closed throughout Race Week, and for some who could not afford to go away during this unpaid holiday there were opportunities of temporary employment as auxiliary drivers on the Corporation trams or bar tenders in the beer tents set up at the racecourse.

On one day a week we attended classes at Doncaster Technical College on full pay. Here we received instruction in machine drawing, applied mechanics, heat engine theory and other subjects leading to a National Certificate in engineering or associated membership of either the Civils or Mechanicals. The following year through the kindness and foresight of our Chief Mechanical Engineer, H. N. Gresley, many of us were privileged to attend works pupils' classes at the Department of Applied Science at Sheffield University. Most of what I know of the theory of heat engines and the testing of materials I learned there, and I am profoundly grateful for having had that opportunity.

From the marking-off table I went on to a double-headed shaping machine. My next move was to the barrel lathe. This was an antiquated machine built by Joseph Whitworth in 1856 and used for producing piston rings from large cast-iron barrels or bushes. The procedure was first to obtain help in rolling the heavy barrel (closely resembling a garden roller in size, shape and weight) up a plank on to the lathe bed, where one of its four lugs was attached to the lathe's faceplate; the other three lugs were brought into line by using the first as a fulcrum and then pulling the faceplate round by hand. Having lightly secured the barrel to the faceplate the lathe was then set in motion and a piece of chalk held steadily against the slowly rotating barrel to show up any eccentricity. It was made to run true by striking it with a 7 lb hammer where the chalk had marked the high spots, and then tightened securely. The twin operations of boring and turning the exterior to gauges was done simultaneously and took 45 minutes. Once the tools were cutting well under the sandy surface, the machine was left unattended while I went down in the materials lift to select another barrel from a heap near the foundry – this gave an opportunity of seeing what was going on elsewhere in the works!

Of particular interest was the locomotive boiler supplying steam to the hammers in the Smithy. This boiler had been taken from one of the American moguls and it was remarkable for its exceptionally narrow firebox necessitated by the bar frames. Two tall columns each terminating in an Ashton pop safety valve were mounted on top of the firebox. Entering other shops if not on legitimate business was firmly discouraged.

On returning to the machine and finding the traverse still satisfactory there was time to gain practice (and not a few bruised and bleeding thumbs) in the use of the hammer and chisel in chipping-off excrescences from the barrel! Parting off the rings, three at a time was effected by three parting tools set *en echelon* in a stout toolholder. With reasonable luck I averaged eight barrels a day and on one occasion succeeded in turning nine, then said to be a record.

It was by such methods and apprentice labour that these ancient machines were able to compete effectively with modern boring mills, and made financial justification for installing these and other newer machinery hard to prove, as I discovered some years later when entrusted with a costing exercise, although the superior quality of the work produced by the new machines was not in doubt.

H. G. Ivatt, at the conclusion of the run by the last of his father's celebrated large Atlantics in 1950, stated that these were built for £2,548 apiece, a phenomenally low price even for 1902. It is interesting to compare this figure with £7,800 given as the cost of building the first Gresley Pacifics twenty years later, and even more so with the approximation quoted by Bert Spencer, (Sir Nigel Gresley's personal draughtman) of £100 for each ton of weight of a Peppercorn Pacific in the late 1940s. The equivalents are 1902 – £21.50 per ton, 1922 – £52.50 per ton, 1948 – £100.00 per ton. Factors affecting these increasing costs of building were the introduction of the 48-hour week, National Health Insurance and unemployment contributions after World War I, and at the time the Peppercorn Pacifics were built the reduction of the working week to 40 hours with paid holidays.

The next move was on to a screw-cutting lathe in Jack Green's gang outside Foreman Treece's office. Here I leaned how to 'square centre' work, do plain turning and later on, screw cutting.

It will be of interest for those accustomed to modern lathes to know how the once universal belt-driven lathe with its neatly stacked pile of change wheels was operated. Each machine had above it a counter shaft driven from the continuously revolving line shaft running the length of the shop. Starting and stopping was effected by pulling down one of two chains operating the striking fork, which moved this belt from the loose to the fast pulley to set the machine in motion. Changes of speed were made by shifting with the aid of belt prop (resembling a domestic linen prop) a second belt connecting two opposed stepped cone pulleys, one on the countershaft and the other driving the lathe mandrel on to the appropriate speed step, that is to say the smallest diameter step of one was opposite the largest diameter step of the other and vice versa. A spanner or hammer shaft was then used to guide the moving belt on to the appropriate step on the lathe pulley – a somewhat dangerous operation!

For screw cutting a compound train of gear wheels was set up bearing the same ratio between driving and driven as that between the thread to be cut and that on the lathe lead screw. It was really remarkable how some turners could give from long experience the correct combination straight away, although quite incapable of making the necessary calculation. The back gear was next put in after disconnecting the drive to the mandrel and chalk marks made on both lead screw and face-plate; when these chalk marks again coincided after the lathe had been set in motion, the lead screw nut could be engaged. Finally, the profile of the thread was finished with a hand chasing tool, which if not applied correctly, gave one a smart crack under the jaw!

Naturally the tyro at turning made the common mistakes and was subject to the usual leg pulls such as being sent to the tool room for a 'putting on' tool when he had removed too much metal from the job in hand! A generation later such a boon did materialise with the introduction of metal spraying. Other stock jokes were to send an unsuspecting youth to Reuben, the toolsmith, with a lead hammer that had become flattened by use, with instructions to have it hardened! – or to be told 'Go down to the boilershop and ask Mr Durrans for a long stand', which he duly got – outside the latter's office!

The last half hour of a Saturday morning was spent cleaning our machines with paraffin and cloths distributed for this purpose, while Wilmot polished the central line shafting till it shone like silver. This he accomplished with an ingenious device consisting of a long iron rod with a polishing pad at its upper extremity which hooked over the shafting, the lower end was turned up to form a seat on which Wilmot rode after the manner of an Alpine chairlift. By exerting a slight twist to the rod he could make it travel along the shaft as if on a screw thread. A similar method was used for polishing piston rods, valve spindles and the like in a lathe by using a large pair of wooden 'nut crackers' with leather hinges embracing a sheet of emery cloth and oil. This was before cylindrical grinders for this purpose became common and micrometers began slowly to replace calipers for taking measurements, though many turners preferred the latter as giving a more sensitive feel.

Work ceased at noon on Saturdays, and then there was a frantic rush by those fortunate enough to be going home for the weekend to get back to their digs, wash and scrub themselves clean in several changes of water, dress hastily and dash back to the station in time to catch the 1.11pm to London!

The railway scene in these early days of the grouping was

extremely interesting. Locomotives and rolling stock in the new L&NER livery were as yet in a minority, and it was still possible to see locomotives and complete trains in the old colours – an exciting experience for one who was born and spent his entire boyhood on the London Brighton & South Coast Railway.

The NER set trains of crimson-lake coaches headed by a handsome Z class three-cylinder Atlantic in spotless pea green paint with much polished brasswork looked particularly fine, as did the Great Central locomotives in Brunswick green with claret frames, seen on the London extension at the head of trains of handsome teak coaches, with raised polished brass numerals and initials.

The Sheffield – Doncaster service saw none of this prestige stock. Ancient hard-riding six-wheelers of Manchester, Sheffield & Lincolnshire ancestry, hauled by Pollitt 4–4–0s with tender weatherboards was the stock in which we travelled to and from Sheffield to attend our weekly works pupils' class at Sheffield University, a salutary reminder that this was part of the old 'Money Sunk & Lost' and not the modernised Great Central Railway.

One evening I had the good fortune to see in the bay platform at Doncaster station one of the pair of four-cylinder compound Atlantics designed for the NER by W. M. Smith, and unusual in having a Belpaire firebox. Another rare visitor was No 2212, the Stumpf uniflow Atlantic, which at speed sounded like a motorcycle with an open exhaust. No 2400, the Raven Pacific remarkable for the length of its boiler and shortness of its connecting rods, also turned up occasionally.

A regular working was the York–Harwich boat train of crimson lake GER coaches brought in by No 1239, one of the NER R1 class enlarged 4–4–0s; this was worked forward at 11.19am by a Great Eastern T19 class rebuilt as a 4–4–0 and resembling a Claud in appearance but with smaller bogie wheels and a single side window cab. These were known as the 'Dolly Grays'.

The GER like the SE&CR had abandoned as a wartime economy measure its handsome and elaborate pre-war livery for unlined lead grey with large numerals on the tender, yellow in the case of the former and white on the latter. Polished brass domes, chimney caps and splasher beadings were all painted over, as on the Great Western, whose locomotives were painted dark green without lining.

It is interesting to record that in 1922 no fewer than six companies painted their coaches a crimson lake – The Midland, Great Eastern, Great Western, North British, North Eastern, South Eastern & Chatham. It was not until 1923 that Brunel's colours were restored to the Great Western main line stock after a lapse of over a decade.

The Great Northern adopted plain unlined lead grey for mineral, freight and shunting locomotives. I distinctly recall to mind the Doncaster station pilot No 1247 in lead grey (now happily preserved by Captain Smith and restored to its pre-1914 apple green) also No 1070, an Ivatt 2–4–0 on the Lincoln service. Atlantics and other passenger engines continued to be painted apple green and lined-out, including the then new 1000 class three-cylinder mixed-traffic engines, which suited their large diameter boilers particularly well. GN coaching stock was varnished teak, and how handsome this looked in the sunlight.

A rare visitor to Doncaster was an LYR radial tank with its train of coaches of a peculiar colour, lower panels a deep plum and the upper ones a dingy snuff colour. This was a durable livery for a line with many smoky tunnels, just as the interior upholstery of slippery horsehair was well adapted to resist the adherence of wool and cotton lint brought in by the Lanky's principal customers, the mill hands of Lancashire and Yorkshire.

During this transition period many interesting experiments were made in trying out on specific duties what had hitherto been regarded as foreign engines. One of these took place on the Leeds line from Doncaster where in turn were tried Great Central No 428C *City of Liverpool* of the Sir Sam Fay class, Great Eastern 1500 class No 1561E resplendent in apple green, a Great Northern 'Ragtimer' of the 1640 class, and lastly another Great Central locomotive, No 6097 *Immingham*. These last two classes seemed to be best suited to this steeply-graded and sharply-curved road.

Another short-lived experiment was the temporary substitution of a Great Central four-cylinder Lord Faringdon class locomotive for the large-boilered Ivatt Atlantics on the new Harrogate Pullman. It was not long before this service reverted to Atlantic haulage, a striking proof of Sturrock's famous dictum that the measure of a locomotive's power is its capacity to boil water, for although the four-cylinder locomotive developed a rated tractive effort at starting of 26,145 lb compared with 17,340 lb for the Atlantic and had 1½ times its adhesion, it could not match with a

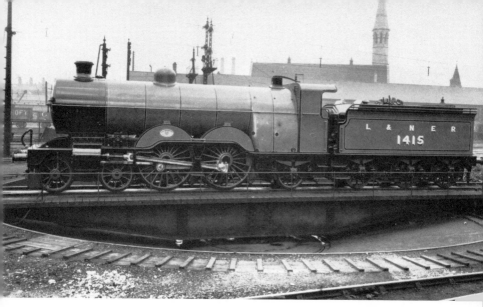

Great Northern Railway Large Atlantic, as LNER No 1415, opposite Doncaster
Plant, with Saint James' Church in the background.

'The brass corner' at Doncaster Works. Note the profusion of machine drive
belts – and not a belt guard in sight – and of cloth caps. One bowler hat appears on
a foreman in the right middle ground.

The lifting shop at King's Cross motive power depot.

Class A1 4–6–2 No 4472 *Flying Scotsman* as originally prepared in high gloss livery for display at the British Empire Exhibition 1924 at Wembley. This was flatted-down to an eggshell finish before the locomotive was put on show.

grate of only 26 sq ft the steam generating capacity of the four-coupled locomotive with its 31 sq ft of grate area.

The Ivatt Atlantics of 1902, subsequently improved by Gresley with the fitting of a 32-element superheater, reigned supreme on the Leeds Pullman for another decade, until strengthening of weak bridges in the Leeds area permitted Pacifics to run over this route. They did their best work on this service, and that decade between 1924 and 1934 was indeed their finest.

Francis Wintour, a tall, commanding, bowler-hatted figure of stern aspect was to be seen at intervals striding through the works on a tour of inspection, accompanied by his Works Manager and Shop Foreman to whom he pointed out with his walking stick items requiring immediate attention. This implement was sometimes used to attract the attention of a workman when the noise and clangour made speech inaudible. 'Pa' Wintour (to distinguish him from his son, Gerald, a premium apprentice) was very much of the old school of railway officer. Typical of his day were the Workshop Rules and Regulations to be observed by workmen employed in the locomotive, carriage and wagon department of the Great Eastern Railway issued in 1890 by James Holden. Rule VIII read:

Attention to Duties
1. Workmen are cautioned against playing or idling during working hours, or washing before the bell rings.
2. No workman is allowed to go into a shop in which he is not usually employed except by order of his foreman.
3. Any workman quarrelling, using improper language, or not cheerfully and carefully carrying out instructions will render himself liable to dismissal.

R. L. Vereker, one time Crimpsall Erecting Shop Manager, told me how in the old days when piecework rates were negotiated individually, Francis Wintour was once accosted as he strode through the smithy by a smith seeking a rise. He listened in silence until they reached the end of the shop then wheeling sharply round and brandishing his stick, ejaculated 'Get away, greedy b————!' Importuning premium apprentices requesting an additional free pass were just as likely to have a paperweight or whatever else came handy hurled at them if they dared to put their heads round his office door. Gerald was often consulted as to what sort of temper the Old Man was in before favours were sought!

This was the background to the attitude of the men in the early 1920s, a high proportion of whom had only recently returned to civilian life after serving and fighting in the 1914–18 war. Men were no longer prepared to accept or tolerate the conditions prevailing before 1914. Hence the prolonged strike of railwaymen in 1919, culminating in the introduction of the eight-hour day and a national agreement on conditions of service, a personal triumph for that skilful negotiator Jimmy Thomas MP, the NUR official.

Whatever their political views, however, they certainly worked hard and saw to it that there was no slacking that could impair piecework earnings, up to the maximum of time-and-a-half; anything beyond this would almost certainly result in a cut in their piecework rate and in a good gang it was customary for this reason to go easy on Thursday, the last day of the working week, which commenced on a Friday.

CHAPTER 2
THE CRIMPSALL

Towards the end of 1924 I was transferred to the Crimpsall Repair Shop built by Henry Ivatt in 1901 for the major overhaul of all Great Northern locomotives, hitherto carried out at the principal running sheds. These up-to-date well-equipped shops comprised four erecting bays each with two pit roads and a centre road for stripping locomotives at the incoming end and wheeling nearly-completed locomotives at the opposite end.

Nos 1, 2 and 3 bays were served by two 35-ton overhead travelling cranes, while No 4 where Pacifics and other heavy three-cylinder locomotives were dealt with had two cranes of 45 tons capacity built by Cravens of Manchester. Between the first and second and third and fourth bays were two narrower bays running the entire length of the shop, that between No 1 and No 2 was a combined machine and fitting shop and the other a boiler and coppersmiths' shop together with a booth for quasi arc-electric welding, at that time an innovation. There was also a section for panel beating, where all dome covers were made, running transversely across the bottom of these bays at the western end was the wheel shop. Beyond this was an electric traverser onto which newly-repaired locomotives were hauled by a capstan for transfer to the paint shop road. Past the traverser was the new tender shop, steaming shed, and parks for the storage of spare wheels and boilers.

Across the middle of the erecting shop ran a central gangway used by the battery-driven tractors hauling trains of material and components to and from the old works, which were a good ten minutes' walk away. I always thought it a pity that we did not have at Doncaster a steam-operated tramway system such as those at Crewe and Horwich, especially on wet days in winter when the passage of a train of these heavily-loaded trucks over the corduroy road composed of old railway sleepers paved with iron soleplates from scrapped coaches would cause pumping and project a jet of muddy icy cold water up one's trouser leg when crossing the works yard.

The Crimpsall was ruled over by a fiery Irishman, R. L. Vereker, a first-rate engineer and a shrewd judge of men, who made frequent sorties into the shop from his elevated office over the gangway to see for himself what was going on. He personally inspected and passed the faced joints of steel steam pipes on Pacifics in the days before lenticular joints rendered unnecessary such meticulous care in facing-up.

'R.L.V.' was Crimpsall Shop Manager for more than 20 years, and I can testify from personal experience that Doncaster locomotives were never better repaired than when he presided there. It was his proud boast that even during the second world war when the output from other works was declining he maintained his weekly output of twelve general repairs.

Early in 1925 I was drafted to Herbert Strangward's pit in No 4 bay, where 4–6–2 No 4472 *Flying Scotsman* was being prepared for the 1925 British Empire Exhibition at Wembley.

The reason for the choice of No 4472 as the LNER exhibit at Wembley the previous year is interesting. As built originally the first batch of Gresley Pacifics had in addition to lightweight motion of nickel-chrome steel, hollow piston rods of the same material forged in one piece with the piston head, thus achieving the maximum reduction in weight of the reciprocating masses. The hollow bore of the piston rod was plugged at the piston head with a screwed plug to take the lathe centre. Due to a fracture in the centre piston rod, No 4472 was out of traffic, and as a result was selected for Wembley, as spares could not be obtained quickly.

Several helpful suggestions were received from some of the older hands as to devices they had used in similar circumstances when preparing Ivatt Atlantic No 1442 for exhibition at the White City in 1909. One was to use a compressed-air drill with a buffing disc attached for polishing axle ends, likewise a cup for polishing the snap head of rivets; both these methods were used on No 4472. In their opinion the finish of No 4472, superlative as we thought it to be, did not quite come up to that of No 1442 (the Royal Engine). A careful scrutiny of photographs taken of both locomotives as exhibited suggests that they may well have been right in their judgement.

Before its departure for Wembley, shrouded in white dust sheets, No 4472 was exhibited at an open day in the paint shop, to which all members of the staff and their families were invited. The photograph shows the locomotive as it then appeared in all its glory of brilliant glossy paintwork, but shortly afterwards this was flatted-down to produce an eggshell finish, as Mr Gresley disliked the multiple reflections produced by the mirror-like brilliance.

The anti-climax produced by No 4472's departure for Wembley, accompanied by Herbert Strangward, was soon forgotten in the ordinary everyday business of overhauling and making fit for long spells of service two of the locomotives in for repair at this time, a three-cylinder 'Tango' mineral engine and an Ivatt superheated 4–4–0 No 3060 on which I subsequently rode to Lincoln on its trial trip.

Locomotives called into the works were stripped at the incoming end of the middle road by Charlie Parker and his gang, who had developed this technique to a fine art – one last pin was knocked out and then all the motion came crashing down into the pit, or so it seemed to we apprentices!

The overhead travelling cranes then lifted the locomotive off its wheels and lowered it onto big baulks of timber placed across the pit assigned for its reception. There it would be worked on steadily for several weeks by an erector and an apprentice until it was ready for wheeling, when the chargehand would increase the workforce to six or perhaps eight men. It was generally reckoned that a locomotive would be completed within a week of being wheeled.

Every endeavour was made to achieve the scheduled weekly output, for if vacant pit spaces were not left for Monday's incoming locomotives piecework earnings, which in a good gang ranged from time-and-a-quarter to time-and-a-third, would suffer accordingly. Bob Whittaker, the foreman of No 2 bay was quite ruthless in this respect and it was not uncommon to see his men working outside (sometimes in the snow) putting-up brake gear on locomotives supposedly finished.

Some of the jobs that came my way were filing up glass-hard axlebox hornblocks with a three-square (triangular) file to a long straight edge and big square, picking out the shells of broken studs with a slender round-nose chisel, facing-up steampipe flanges to a surface plate with the aid of a scraper, and splitting seized nuts in awkward corners of smokeboxes with hand hammer and chisel, when the advantage of becoming ambidextrous became painfully obvious.

Another skill to acquire was the ability to swing a quarter (7 lb) hammer for driving in (or out) turned bolts, or splitting seized nuts with a chisel bar. The day of the big hammer man has long since passed, but until the oxy-acetylene cutting torch came into common use, the ability to swing a heavy hammer either right- or left-handed with force and precision was an essential part of a fitter's training. One technique was similar to swinging a golf club – arms straight, hands grasping the shaft near its extremity and swinging from the shoulders. Another and less tiring method was to raise the hammer with hands apart, allowing the shaft to slide through the hand nearest the head when the blow was being delivered, and relying on the other for guidance.

Much was to be learned of other trades. It was fascinating to watch the skill and team work of a boilermaker, holder-up and rivet boy. The boy would take a glowing white-hot rivet from his portable hearth with a pair of tongs, toss it towards the holder-up who caught it dexterously at the top of its trajectory in a small pan or shovel, thrust it into the hole to be filled and apply to it his heavy holding-up tool, whereupon the boilermaker would strike at it fiercely with his rivetting hammer before the rivet had time to cool. This operation was repeated faultlessly scores of times and thought of as nothing remarkable.

It was intriguing to watch a plater inserting a new section of plate. This would be sheared to size, then offered-up into place and the position of existing rivet holes marked on it with a piece of tube dipped into a pan of white paint and then inserted in the rivet hole. The plate thus marked would then be taken to the punching machine whose powerful toggle action knocked out a plug of smoking metal as easily as a ticket inspector punches a hole in a cardboard ticket.

The same machine was also used for nibbling plates to an outline, a duty performed much quicker and better today by profile-cutting machines. Holes in boiler plates and patches were always drilled for two good reasons – because it was more accurate and avoids the use of a drift to align holes, and because drilling left no residual stresses in the plate from which fractures could start. I believe that this method of construction and the use of lap joints persisted in American boiler practice long after it had been abandoned in Europe.

Boilermakers are by repute a tough breed and the fact that they were on piecework did not encourage their rivet lads to neglect their duties or lark about. There was one rivetter a tall, swarthy man with a cruel expression, whom I saw make his rivet lad pick up a nearly red hot rivet snap that the lad had idly projected from his pneumatic hammer by twisting his ear until the lad seared his fingers in the attempt. Even in those days this was going a bit too far and brought remonstrances from other workmen.

Before the ready-cut asbestos joint came into general use a job for the apprentices was the manufacture of joints from iron wire gauze or india rubber reinforced with canvas (india rubber insertion) according to whether these were for steam or water. A roll of wire gauze sufficient to make all the joints in a smokebox, was obtained from the stores together with a large lump of red lead putty (a mixture of red and white lead). A piece of gauze was placed on the flange for which the joint was required and its outline tapped out with a hammer, using the ball pein to mark the bolt holes. The gauze was then cut to shape with an old pair of scissors and its surface liberally spread with the red lead putty using a 1 ft rule as a spatula. The joints thus prepared were then hung on the smokebox door dart until required, in order to prevent them becoming contaminated with soot or grit. No material was wasted, smaller joints were cut from the circles knocked out from the larger joints. The addition of a single strand of asbestos string laid inside the circle of stud holes was commonly used for the larger joints such as dome covers and boiler manholes, which were apt to give trouble with blowing, and I have also seen cast-iron borings kneaded into the putty with the same object in view.

Another variant that I found in use at King's Cross top shed was the sandwich joint – two sheets of graphited asbestos paper reinforced with a sandwich of gauze wire in between. This was an excellent joint and much used for those locomotives with steamchest cover joints in the smokebox, such as the 'Long Toms' and GC 'Pom-poms'. I have sometimes wondered why we did not contract lead poisoning through kneading the red lead putty with sooty hands, pricked and bleeding from cutting the wire gauze, but we seemed to thrive on it. Skin complaints such as dermatitis were a rarity until the coming of diesel traction and the use of fuel oil.

Jobs inaccessable to full-grown men, such as crawling into a fully tubed boiler in order to remove injector delivery pipe clips after the regulator head and J pipe had been removed, or along the narrow water legs of saddle tanks, were recognised tasks for apprentices, especially those of small or slim stature. A tallow dip screwed into a ⅝in nut for a candlestick was the only portable illuminant at that time and even today the smell of hot tallow still revives memory of near panic when struggling to get out of the confined space in a fully tubed boiler.

There was one small puny lad, a coppersmith's apprentice, who was in great demand as a retriever of nuts or tools that had accidently fallen down blastpipes. I can still picture him in the smokebox with his arm buried up to the shoulder in a cylinder exhaust cavity, like a terrier in a rat hole, while two hulking great erectors stood over him and encouraged him in his efforts.

Two interesting locomotives, both Atlantics, came in for general repairs round about this time. The first was Ivatt's four-cylinder compound large Atlantic No 292, remarkable for its two reversing levers placed side by side, one for the high-pressure system and the other for the low-pressure. There was also a flag marked with a brass star on the right high pressure steamchest to indicate to the driver the position of the changeover valve. Notching-up No 292 must have been quite a feat of strength, and I suspect that none but the keenest drivers ventured to alter the reversers once these were set, but throttled at the regulator, thus nullifying any advantage from the compound expansion. Twenty-five years later when riding on one of Bulleid's Battle of Britain class, I was to see a pressure of 280 lb in the boiler throttled down to 80 lb in the steamchest for the same reason, the driver's understandable reluctance to alter the temperamental steam reverser at speed. In both instances a screw reverser would have enabled these locomotives to develop their real potential.

The second locomotive that came in was No 271, a Klondyke or small-boilered Atlantic built by Ivatt, originally as a four-cylinder simple but later rebuilt as an inside-cylinder superheated Atlantic, utilising a pair of 55 class piston valve cylinders – No 271 had the reputation of being exceptionally fast.

Errands to other parts of the works afforded a wonderful opportunity of inspecting the line of locomotives by the river bank, awaiting scrapping. I remember particularly No 770N, a Stirling 0-4-4 side tank rebuilt with a domed boiler and still in GNR green. This like most Stirling locomotives and many of Ivatt's design had the boiler backhead flush with the cab weatherboard, thus making the cab much longer than its external appearance would suggest. This increased distance made it necessary to link the vacuum brake ejector application handle on the boiler front to a second handle on the cab side to enable the brake to be applied when looking out. The last survivor of this class that long outlived the others was the Doncaster Works crane locomotive, which had two short side tanks at either side of its smokebox to counterbalance the 5-ton steam crane mounted on its bunker for lifting and transporting heavy weights like cylinder castings about the works.

Other interesting machines seen on the scrap road were the four small steam railmotors complete with their coaches, Nos 1 and 2, Doncaster-built and Nos 5 and 6 by Kitson. Of especial interest was No 1300, the one time four-cylinder de Glehn compound Atlantic built by the Vulcan Foundry and later converted to simple propulsion with a pair of K2 pattern outside cylinders; it still retained its original and unique boiler with a raised round-top narrow firebox. Absence of the inside low-pressure cylinders made it possible by crouching down and looking over the bogie centre casting, to see right back to the firebox.

Breaking-up condemned engines was done by a remarkable character, rejoicing in the nickname of Rakko, whose favourite weapon was a long-shafted quarter hammer that he affectionately addressed as 'von Fritz'! Even this implement expertly wielded could make little impression on cylinder castings, and these were demolished to foundry size by dropping onto them a heavy cast-iron ball suspended from a sheerlegs, equipped with a quick release device. Copper fireboxes were removed by cutting or breaking off the stays with powerful long stroke compressed-air guns; all very different to what happens today.

The year 1925 stands out in my memory for several notable events, first the thrill of preparing No 4472 for the British Empire Exhibition, and then the arrival at Doncaster of Inspector Flewellyn with GWR 4-6-0 No 4079 *Pendennis Castle* and the excitement of the Interchange Trials, treated by the press as a kind of sporting event. To be well and truly beaten on our own ground by the GWR locomotive was a chastening experience, but the lesson was thoroughly learned. Within two years the application to all Gresley Pacifics of the modified valve gear devised by Bert Spencer in 1924 brought down the coal consumed per mile from around 50 lb to 35.38 lb, thus making possible the non-stop runs to Edinburgh in 1928.

Earlier in the year Patrick Stirling's celebrated 8ft single No 1, stored at King's Cross top shed since the International Exhibition at Sheperd's Bush in 1909, arrived at Doncaster for restoration to working order for the Centenary Celebrations to be held at Darlington in July. The boiler was merely an empty shell without tubes or firebox, and search was made throughout the GNR system for a replacement straightback or domeless boiler. One was ultimately found supplying steam to the grease factory at the Decoy (marshy land), and brought back to Doncaster works where it was fitted into No 1 in the old erecting shop in which the locomotive had been built 55 years earlier. It was decided to restore it as far as possible to its original condition. Ancient drawings were brought out and replica parts made. A low-sided Sturrock tender with outside frames was also found and fitted with wooden brake blocks. When No 1 finally emerged from the paint shop resplendent in a new coat of apple green and was put in steam, I contrived to get a ride up and down the paint shop road; how slowly those great driving wheels revolved, compared with those of an Atlantic!

Premium apprentices enjoyed the privilege at three-monthly intervals of accompanying a locomotive on which they had worked on its trial trip. The usual destinations were Grantham for Pacifics, Retford for tank engines, Lincoln for all other classes, and occasionally Leeds. My turn came one sunny morning in late spring when I was booked to accompany Class D1 4-4-0 No 3060 to Lincoln and back with Fred Elms, a pleasant fatherly man and one of the three regular trial trip drivers at the locomotive weighhouse. Like most beginners, my first attempts at firing were clumsy and awkward, but improved when shown the correct stance and how that by keeping the foot nearest to the shovelling plate in one position and turning the body by pivoting on that heel, it was possible to pick up the coal and add at the same time impetus to the shovel's swing in a follow-through stroke. Lincoln Cathedral perched on its hill, looking like a ship at sea, appeared on the horizon all too soon and warned that we were nearing our destination and the fire was run down accordingly. The homeward run was quite fast and the click of the rail joints was the only sound audible, sure proof that the locomotive was in good nick.

The eagerly-awaited Railway Centenary Celebrations at Darlington took place on 2 July 1925 and those premium apprentices wishing to attend were given passes, also a day's leave with pay. On arrival early in the morning at Darlington my companion and I set out immediately to secure a good vantage point at the lineside, for even at that hour people were flocking there and several enterprising farmers with fields adjoining the railway were charging motorists 6d (2½p) for entry, an early example of parking fees. We finally chose a lineside fence with a good view in each direction, within sight of the commodious covered grandstand that had been erected at Eaglescliffe for distinguished guests.

The procession of 54 locomotives, eight drawing trains, led by Nicholas Wood's Hetton Colliery engine of 1822, albeit extensively rebuilt in the 1880s, was due to leave Stockton at 11.00am. I shall never forget my first sight of its grasshopper beams rising and falling, nor the roar of the cheering spectators as it came into view on passing the grandstand, a spectacle that I was to see repeated half a century later in Mike Satow's splendid replica of *Locomotion No 1* in the Rail 150 Cavalcade.

The Hetton Colliery engine was followed by the old *Derwent*, remarkable for its additional tender at the chimney end, on which the fireman rode in order to fire the return-flue boiler. This was a design developed especially for mineral traffic on the Stockton & Darlington Railway by Timothy Hackworth, the first locomotive superintendent. These two veterans, manned by enginemen attired in period uniforms complete with top hats, received special applause as they trundled past with a feather of steam blowing from their safety valves.

To describe in detail every one of the 54 interesting and spendidly restored examples of British locomotive development that took part in this pageant would be tedious and unnecessary, but it is interesting to reflect that in 1925 the single was not extinct, and of those exhibited the Johnson Spinner could still be seen piloting trains into St Pancras, while the GCR Pollitt single had been working on the Cheshire lines between Liverpool and Manchester.

Towards the end of 1925 I was transferred temporarily to the wheel shop to take micrometer readings of the taper and ovality of locomotive journals, a procedure just introduced to take advantage of the greater accuracy possible with the recently installed Churchill journal grinder. Another acquisition was a modern heavy-duty tyre-turning lathe by Buckton's that could top and profile a pair of 68in diameter tyres in 50 minutes.

In contrast, at the opposite end of the shop was an ancient lathe with faceplates 9ft 0in in diameter, formerly used for turning the wheels of the Stirling 8ft singles. This lathe also had a special radially-mounted tool holder for turning the hour-glass-shaped journals of Stirling tenders, a self-centring device working on the same principal as the Cartazzi radial axlebox.

Another interesting machine was the wheel balancer, a replica of that in use at Swindon. It was fascinating to watch a pair of 80in diameter wheels in the machine whizzing round so steadily that not a drop of water would be spilled from a brimfull tumbler placed on the sensitive spring-supported bearings. The findings of the Bridge Stress Committee had brought to light the detrimental effect of hammer-blow on bridges and track and the wheel-balancing machine was in constant use for re-balancing wheels from the several constituent companies not fortunate enough to possess such a machine, including the Southern Railway, which sent a set of King Arthur wheels.

After the wheel shop interlude I returned to the work of locomotive repairing in No 4 bay, this time on Wilson's pit where I assisted in the complete general repairs of condensing Class N1 0–6–2T No1561, and the pioneer Class O1 2–8–0 No 3456.

When making out my weekly piecework voucher, I was instructed by my chargehand as to what locomotive numbers to put down. Nos 1561 and 3456 were not among them as the low wages of an apprentice were very helpful in offsetting the cost of some unexpected job that an adult erector encountered and which would adversely affect his balance or bonus. In a well organised gang this would usually be at the rate of time-and-one-third, but the most that I received as an apprentice was the guaranteed time-and-one-quarter for preparing *Flying Scotsman* for the British Empire Exhibition, until I went boiler mounting when I was cautioned to go easy on a Thursday 'Lest our rate be cut' – almost a certainty if more than time-and-a-half was earned. Conversely, should an erecting gang get into debt to the extent of (say) £20 as one particular gang did, it would receive no more balance until the debt was paid off or until it was written-off by the works manager as an act of clemency.

I was still on Wilson's pit at the start of the General Strike in May 1926, reporting for duty as usual, as did all the other premiums apart from the more senior who had volunteered and been accepted for footplate duties.

An uncanny silence reigned in the Crimpsall, deserted except for ourselves and a handful of supervisors. Time dragged heavily as we worked at such jobs as we could do single-handed, completely isolated from the exciting events going on outside the works. We stuck this for three days, then learning that volunteers from outside were being accepted for footplate work we went *en masse* to see the works manager to volunteer for 'active service.' Mr Eggleshaw gave us a sympathetic hearing and immediately sent us to see Mr Oakes, the District Locomotive Superintendent at the Carr Sheds, who explained that although all footplate vacancies had been filled volunteers were required for steam raising, boiler washing, barring and other shed duties.

Bob Coates and I decided on steam raising as the next best thing to firing a locomotive and reported at the Carr shed for duty at 10.00pm the same night. There we were shown how to test the water gauges, apply the injectors and cover the grate with coal, leaving a bare spot in the middle where several scoopsful of live fire taken from the sand furnace, were placed. That and subsequent nights passed quickly enough and we stayed long after the proper finishing time at 6.00am in order to greet and hand over our charges to the crews coming on duty. Among these was R. L. Vereker, manager of the Crimpsall, whose Atlantic I was determined should not be lacking in steam when he arrived. It had in fact been blowing-off hard at intervals for most of the night through my excess zeal! Naturally enough there were some anxious moments when there was difficulty in getting an injector to work, with the water bobbing in the bottom nut and a good fire in the box.

I still have two of the lists of locomotives that we tended. The first comprises seventeen – two passenger and the remainder mixed-traffic and six-coupled goods – while the second totals 27 and includes five passenger engines, an indication of the increase in traffic as volunteers became more experienced and better organised.

At the end of one of these nightly vigils, the Class J3 0–6–0 that I was tending was boarded by its volunteer driver, a colliery official who asked me if I would be kind enough to explain the controls to him as he was working a train to Sheffield and was unfamiliar with railway engines. This set me thinking furiously – if he can drive why not me? The upshot was an interview with Inspector Trotter who opined that I would want to drive at 80mph like all the rest! I reassured him on this point and then retired to my digs for food and rest. I reported for duty as usual the same night and it was not until my stint of steam raising was nearly over that I found to my surprise and delight that I was booked driver of the 6.00am Station Pilot! The fact that I had been on duty all night (my own fault, I should have examined the list) worried me not at all and I hastened to find and prepare No 3589, a superheated six-coupled goods fitted with top feed delivering into the boiler through clackboxes attached to a second dome, forward of that containing the regulator. My fireman, a man at least twice my age who said he had fired traction engines in America, helped me to prepare No 3589 for the road. We filled every oil cup within sight including those on the valve spindle dummy glands, which obviously served no useful purpose as they were full of smokebox char and had been for a long time. Both injectors were of the lifting or faceplate pattern, standard on both Great Northern and Great Central locomotives and those of many other companies at that time – easy and convenient to work if well maintained but a nightmare to a fireman when condensation was destroyed by a leaking steam valve or clack. A sticking clack can sometimes be re-seated by tapping its cap nut with a hammer. Those on No 3589, being attached to the dome, meant that the fireman had to leave the footplate, clamber along the boiler to reach them if they stuck, which generally happened at the most inconvenient moment.

We set off tender-first, for the station, where we picked up our shunter who showed me how to set a vacuum-fitted locomotive on a turntable by giving a little steam before releasing the brake and then re-applying it as the locomotive started to roll.

There was quite a large audience of strikers on Marshgate bridge but fortunately for my self esteem we were out of earshot of their comments on my beginner's attempts at balancing a locomotive on a turntable. I was just getting the hang of shunting coaches when with the utmost reluctance I had to hand over to a relief driver who said that I had been on duty long enough. I was booked station pilot again on the day following and was really enjoying myself when the strike came to an end, and it was back to the Crimpsall and the normal routine. I had one encounter with strike pickets, all attired in clean overalls and uniform caps, who behaved in a gentlemanly and correct way and allowed me to pass when I explained that I was a premium apprentice, not in any trade union, and that it was my duty to continue working as to do otherwise would be disloyal and most likely prejudice my chances of employment at the end of my apprenticeship.

Repairing dead engines seemed very dull work after the excitement of working with those in steam during the general strike, but this was soon forgotten when my turn came for a two-month spell learning how to set valves.

The course of instruction on heat engines, valve gears and valve diagrams that I was currently studying at Sheffield University under Mr Davis and which I found so interesting was now to have a practical application, and what better tutor could I have than George Simpson, confidant of the drawing office and acknowledged expert on setting valves? Valve setting and valve gear problems have always fascinated me and I should like here to record my gratitude to those who taught me my trade, and gave freely of their hard-won knowledge in answer to my questions. Only once during my apprenticeship was I told to 'Find out for thy sen lad, I 'ad to!' (Sen' = Yorkshire dialect word for 'self.') Incidentally, it was George Simpson who lent me his prized copy of George Hughes' classic work on locomotive erection.

I was first shown how to transfer the port marks to the valve spindle, directly in the case of slide valves by means of a feeler gauge and indirectly for inside admission piston valve with the aid of a measuring staff. The next step was to quarter the wheel in order to obtain the four dead centres (six in the case of a three-cylinder engine) and finally the leads and port openings were taken for specific cut-offs in both forward and backward gears.

Unlike a running shed where the locomotive has its coupling rods on and has to be moved bodily backwards and forwards by a gang of men with pinch bars, the works practice was to put on only the connecting rods, and then by raising the driving wheels just clear of the rails to rotate the wheels with either a hand ratchet, or in later years, an electrically-driven device. In my day it was the hand ratchet, and hard work it was, especially under a small wheel inside-cylinder locomotive where one had to crouch down to avoid the eccentrics and big-end cranks. When quartering the wheel on a three-cylinder locomotive the wheel had to be stopped with precision twelve times in every revolution, and this ordeal caused poor George much anguish, for he was afflicted with a bad stammer. When after much facial contortion he eventually succeeded in producing a long drawn-out 'Whoa', the centre had gone well past the trammel. There was then much bad language from the labourer on the ratchet, who had to reverse direction and come forward again in order to eliminate the effect of any lost motion in the bearing. I have wondered sometimes why George did not strike a bell or gong as a signal to stop – after all, the great engines of a ship are controlled in this manner.

Locomotives were normally set with equal leads but on express types the piston displacement at the points of cut-off on both in stroke and out stroke were also measured. Should these differ by more than ¾in, the cut-offs were equalised at the expense of the leads, due allowance being made for expansion when hot. I had therefore a good opportunity of seeing the various types of valves then in use, such as the plain D slide valve, or the Richardson balanced slide valves fitted to the Atlantics and Long Toms. These exhausted through the back of the valve and had four spring-loaded cast-iron balancing strips, arranged like an Oxford picture frame.

Piston valves were mainly of the broad ring type like the Schmidt with its trick ports connected by a long tubular duct between the heads. Locomotives thus fitted were usually provided with another Schmidt speciality, the piston tail rod to support the heavy cast-steel piston heads and prevent these from scoring the cylinders, and later discarded as unnecessary, like the superheater element dampers before them.

Some, perhaps all, Class K3 locomotives had the Canadian Pacific Railway type piston valve, a plain broad ring, eccentric in section, that is thickest opposite the gap, pierced with numerous ⅛in diameter holes, said to be for the release of water. The now universal Knorr type narrow multi-valve (another German invention) was just being applied experimentally to a few Class N2 condensing Metropolitan Tanks. I remember marvelling at the sight of a new Churchill grinder with a magnetic chuck, then a novelty, for grinding these narrow rings to the requisite thickness for the grooves.

In later years I was to find out the hard way that for every advantage there is a corresponding disadvantage and the price paid for the superior steam-tightness of the narrow multi-ring valves was the great difficulty sometimes experienced in extracting them as compared with the broad ring type, due to an accumulation of carbon under the rings, which must be crushed before the valve can be withdrawn.

Doncaster Works crane locomotive, scrapped *circa* 1927.

Great Central Railway 'Pom Pom' 0–6–0 as LNER No 5226.

Class N2 0–6–2T No 4747, hauling a double quad-art passenger set.

CHAPTER 3

MILLWRIGHTS' AND ERECTING SHOP

After spending nearly two years on locomotive repairs amid the noise and hustle of the Crimpsall, a transfer to the peace and quietness of the millwrights' shop made a pleasant change. This, known as Tom Smith's Shop after its foreman, was responsible for the maintenance in good condition of all the machinery and appliances in the plant, and its highly-skilled staff were the only ones to work during Race Week, overhauling vital machine tools while their operators were on holiday.

I was fortunate in working alongside Arthur Kenyon, who I believe had been an artificer in the Royal Navy; he certainly had the requisite bearing and quiet assurance of one insisting always on workmanship of the highest standard. He was sometimes to be seen walking through the shop deep in thought and it was said that he was then looking for the lost 'thous' (1/1000in!).

The task given to me was the repair and overhaul of compressed-air drills. These were of two types, a four-cylinder V engine like a miniature motorcycle engine (of these the Ingersoll Rand and Consolidated Pneumatic were examples) and a local product, the Bradford air drill, driven by a vane motor similar to a modern exhauster on a diesel railcar and used for drilling out boiler stays.

I also helped in the conversion from hand to electric operation of a wagon hoist at the Decoy Wagon Shops, and saw for the first time how simple appliances like a telegraph pole and rope blocks were used to lift the heavy electric winch into position. On its proving trial the regular operator, so accustomed to giving orders to his crew at the winch handles, caused much laughter when he

(*left*) GNR Class W long firebox 4–4–0 No 1361.
Class N2 0–6–2T with early post-Grouping number 1722N.
Class N7 0–6–2T No 996E, with short-travel valves. The driver is B. Smith.

shouted 'Whoa!' to the machine when he wanted it to stop!

The wagon shops (now occupied by Fordson Tractors) are situated on marshy ground in an isolated locality known as the Decoy, about two miles south of Doncaster station. Workmen were conveyed to and from by the 'Pike Island Express', a train of ancient four-wheel suburban coaches painted red brown and hauled by an elderly Stirling straight-back goods engine. A unique feature of the wagon shops was the cloakroom arrangements. Outer garments were hung on hooks attached to beams suspended from the roof by ropes and pulleys – as soon as the buzzer blew to start work beams and garments were hoisted high above the shop floor and not lowered again until finishing time. The reasons given for this unusual arrangement were economy of space and prevention of pilfering. A parody of this procedure performed on the stage of the local theatre brought vociferous applause from the many wagon builders present.

Seen also at the wagon shops was a funeral pyre on which horse drawn drays were being burned – an indicator of the changing pattern of road transport in the mid-1920s. About the same time two or three Foden steam wagons still labelled GNR came into the plant for repairs. These, probably the last steam wagons to be repaired, emerged in LNER blue livery with scarlet red wheels, and were given a road test up a steep hill at nearby Warmsworth.

Some of the railway's traffic lost during the General Strike was never recaptured and this, coupled with increasing road transport competition, meant that fewer locomotives and rolling stock were needed, and consequently fewer staff to repair them. Temporary shift staff taken-on to overhaul arrears of maintenance resulting from the war were discharged and many shops put on short time.

By the time I went into the New Erecting Shop the first batch of Pacifics built to the LNER loading gauge (Nos 2543–62) had been completed and work was proceeding on a further series of Ardsley Tanks, six-coupled shunting locomotives with long sloping side tanks, of GNR design dating back to 1912.

Matthew Burton, foreman of the New Shop and chargehand erector Matt Nisbet were both nearing retirement and I was especially fortunate in working under the latter, then building his 405th locomotive. Building orders were usually for batches of ten, shared between two pits running the length of the shop and once the first had been built the others followed in regular sequence. A locomotive a week, a coach a day and a wagon an hour was the

Victorian works manager's target, and with a simple straightforward design like the J50 shunting tank this was achieved.

The several stages of erection were roughly as follows. First a pair of 1⅛in steel frame plates, slotted in batches of eight in the machine shop would be brought in and laid flat on trestles for the hornblocks or axlebox guides to be fitted. The next stage was to set up the frames on bottle jacks, using temporary tubular stays to keep them parallel to one another, then to position them accurately for the reception of the cylinders, motion plate, dragbox and other parts. In building a locomotive the accurate alignment of the frames and cylinders was of prime importance, and great pains were taken to achieve this by means of big squares, long straight edges, diagonal trammelling and piano wires stretched taut through the centre lines of the cylinders. Next, the holes for the bolts securing the cylinders, dragbox etc, were reamed-out full size and turned pan-head bolts driven in, any slight inaccuracy found in axlebox hornblock alignment being rectified by filing.

After this, erection went on apace. Slidebars were put up and aligned, weighbar shaft and reversing quadrant installed, valves and pistons put in and boxed-up ready for the boiler (previously lagged) to be lowered into the frame. Once the boiler was in and the tanks on, the platers could get busy rivetting the cab superstructure and coal bunker, while the erectors put in the steampipes and aligned the chimney with the blastpipe. Meanwhile the coppersmiths were fitting injector and lubricator pipes, the painters were at work painting and lining-out the frames while these were still accessible. Finally the nearly completed locomotive was lifted by the overhead travelling cranes and lowered on to its wheels, which had arrived with axleboxes already fitted from the wheel shop.

Up to this stage an erector and an apprentice had managed to keep pace with the work but after wheeling, extra hands were put on to finish the locomotive. Unlike the Crimpsall, each erector set his own valves under the supervision of the shop foreman. I followed this procedure through in its entirety on Nos 1079 and 1086 and found the absence of grime, oil and soot inseparable from repairing locomotives in the Crimpsall an agreeable change.

My chief recollection of the New Shop concerns fitting the massive cast steel hornblocks into the frames, possibly on account of their great weight. First of all the machined edges of the hornblock were lightly smeared with red raddle marking and it was then pushed into the tapered horn gap in the frame as far as it would go; depending how far this was from its final position, the edges of the gap were carefully filed, or perhaps a light chipping removed from the tapered or wedge side.

Steam locomotives, although sometimes built in large numbers, were never mass-produced like motor cars, and inevitably there were minute variations in the dimensions of components. The astute fitter or erector chose those parts that demanded the minimum of work in fitting, consequently the last locomotive in a batch would entail more work than the preceding ones.

I was very glad that I had become proficient in the art of chipping, so that the chisel marks needed only the minimum amount of filing to remove them. Matt Nisbet quite rightly insisted on a high standard of workmanship and did not rely solely on the evidence of feeler gauges to assess the quality of a fit, but would hold the flame of a lighted tallow candle below the joint edge; it was quite astonishing how many hollow places its penetrating smoke exposed!

Another instance of Matt's method of training occurred during the slack period between locomotive orders when a large-boilered Atlantic came into the shop for new cylinders and half frames. Another apprentice and I were given the task of driving in the 1¼in diameter pan-heated cylinder bolts. Finding it easier to strike them directly with a quarter hammer instead of interposing a punch bar as we should have done, left our trade mark in crescent-shaped indentations on a few of the bolt heads. The penalty for this lapse from grace was having to remove these marks with a file and restore the true conical shape of the heads – a lesson that I have never forgotten.

I did not see the completion of the next batch of N7 0–6–2T of GER design, for in June of 1927 I left Doncaster to gain experience at the running sheds.

CHAPTER 4

RUNNING SHED EXPERIENCE

My request was granted to be allocated to a London depot so that I could live at home in North London for the period of my running shed training. On a sunny June morning in 1927 I reported at the former Great Central Railway depot at Neasden, then commanded by Mathew Dalton Robinson, son of the last chief mechanical engineer of the Great Central.

Some changes had taken place in the seven years since a visit in 1920. It was then still very much a country depot on the outskirts of London with allotment gardens and open fields to the north westward, a landscape that finally disappeared only when it was engulfed by the coming of the North Circular Road and light industry. In 1927, although one sensed that changes were impending, it was still possible to enjoy a real country pub lunch of cold boiled beef, beer and pickles seated under a chestnut tree in the garden of 'The Spotted Dog', at that time still a typical south country clapboard inn with benches outside.

As far as the depot was concerned, little had changed apart from the livery of the locomotives. The A5 tanks were now LNER black but lined-out in true Great Central goods engine style of black with a broad red line edged by two fine white lines – such was the pride in the traditions of the old companies that persisted long after the 1923 Grouping.

Compared with my Doncaster digs, living at home seemed like sheer luxury, even if it did mean getting up early in order to be at Neasden in time for the 7.30am start. I enjoyed too the journey by the Metropolitan Railway in its clerestory-roof American-style cars furnished with rattan covered seats and hand-operated sliding doors. During the warm weather these were often left open while running – another inducement to live in Metroland.

Everything at Neasden was so completely different from my previous experience that it was like starting afresh on another railway, for that is exactly what it was – the GREAT CENTRAL RAILWAY! Not only the locomotives but the men and their customs were different, too. The busy clangour of the works was exchanged for the thrilling hiss of steam from open cylinder cocks as locomotives moved out of the smoky shed on to the preparation pits outside. The roar of steam escaping from safety valves as firemen made up their fires inspired a sense of urgency and impatience, lacking from more modern forms of traction.

Working conditions also were very different from those in the works, for here there was a constant movement of locomotives in and out of the shed. This brought home the vital importance of protecting oneself against accidental movement of the locomotive one was going to repair, by seeing first that it was not coupled to others on the same road and then by affixing 'NOT TO BE MOVED' boards or warning targets to its opposite corners.

All the running sheds on the Great Central's London Extension were alike, and a description of Neasden will serve to illustrate them all. Covered accommodation for approximately half the allocation was provided by a six-road shed of the dead-end type sited at some distance from and at an angle to the main line. The running foremen's cabin, the control centre of any running shed was strategically placed about midway down the yard where the six shed roads converged, enabling the foreman to regulate the order of departure of the locomotives, which often left coupled two and three together with the one for the most distant destination in the lead. Locomotives returning to shed also passed the cabin on their way to the turntable, coal stage and ashpits, and their crews were instructed on which shed road to place them so that each road could be built up in the correct order of departure for the next day's work. Those leaving at nearly the same time were not put on the same road for should the first locomotive fail, it would almost certainly delay the one behind it. The foreman had a shed turner or shunter and a set of shed enginemen to assist in marshalling the shed when the crews could not be used for berthing their charges.

Coaling was done manually from an elevated stage, a massive structure of blue brick supporting the depot's water storage tank of 100,000 gallons capacity. Wagons of coal were propelled up a steeply inclined ramp to the elevated stage and their contents shovelled into steel tubs on wheels, each holding half a ton; these were wheeled on to a kind of chute or drawbridge so contrived as to allow their contents to be tipped into the tenders or bunkers of the locomotives waiting below.

So much for the general layout. Alongside the shed and combined in its structure was a series of buildings used for the following purposes.

First the depot superintendent's office, with its steps neatly whitewashed and a large bay window overlooking the shed front and yard, from which 'the Guv'nor' could keep an eye on departures and enquire immediately into any late starts.

Then came the general office with an inner glazed pen for the chief clerk; this was followed by the timekeeper, duty list clerk's office and enginemen's messroom. The oil and material stores came next. The oil tanks were arranged at a height that drums of oil could be rolled staight out of a wagon standing outside the through a doorway in the stores wall and their contents emptied by gravity into the storage tanks below, so eliminating the need for pumping. It also enabled empty barrels to be reloaded in the same wagon, thereby reducing demurrage charges on drums and wagons.

Beyond the stores was the blacksmiths' shop presided over by a portly smith named George Bratton and shared by him with the boilersmiths. Beyond this again came the machine shop, containing the usual machine tools, centre lathes, drilling machines and I believe a shaper and of course the wheel lathe, facing an archway through which wheels were rolled from the drop tables on Nos 1 and 2 roads. Last in the line of buildings came the hot water washing-out plant supplied with steam from an old locomotive boiler.

A long fitting bench ran transversely across the end wall of this dead-end shed, broken only by a doorway in the centre leading to the coppersmiths' shop, whose occupant like all his breed, a highly skilled but generally testy individual (was it the coke fumes that made them so?) would lock the door and open only to Ted Claxton, the leading fitter.

Two small wooden hutches, little bigger than sentry boxes, one in each corner of this end wall served as offices for the leading fitter and for his opposite number, the leading boilersmith. The fitters' cupboards alongside the shed wall had their tops inclined at 45°, an excellent idea that effectively prevented the storage of assorted rubbish that usually accumlates on top of lockers. Finally, on the far side of the shed was a small messroom for the artisan staff, its deal tables and benches kept spotlessly clean by daily scrubbing with soap, sand and hot water.

The accident train comprising a Cowans Sheldon 15-ton steam crane, tool and packing vans and a standard Great Central bogie riding and mess van was kept under cover on No 6 road with a slow fire in the boiler, ready for instant use.

My introduction to running shed work was in helping old Jimmy Simmonds (who was uncertain of his age) to remove the driving wheels from an early Director class locomotive No 5433 *Walter Burgh Gair* on the drop table. This appliance was standard at all the Great Central new line sheds and was the antecedent of the modern wheel drop: a decade later I was to find similar appliances in use in the running sheds of the Nigerian Railway.

The drop table consisted of a long stroke hydraulic jack sunk into the bottom of the inspection pit, its ram terminating in a massive T-shaped head or table having ledges at its sides on which the flanges of the wheels to be lowered rested yet narrow enough for this head to pass between the rails. The operation of lowering wheels was as follows. First the hydraulic pumps driven from the adjacent machine shop line shafting were set in motion and the drop table raised sufficiently for two removable sections of rail about 7ft 6in long to be taken out. The wheels were then lowered far enough for the spring gear to be disconnected and finally to the pit bottom for the axlebox to be removed. Unlike the wheel drop where the wheels are lowered well below rail level so that the locomotive can be drawn off to allow the wheels to be raised to the surface, this could not be done in the case of the drop table and the work of refitting axleboxes proceeded under the locomotive. There was barely sufficient clearance between the axle and the lower corners of the horns in which to rotate an axlebox. Conveniently, Great Central locomotives had steel axlebox shells with removable square brasses, which after re-metalling and re-boring were bedded onto a cylindrical cast-iron dummy of appropriate diameter at the bench. It was only with the solid bronze box that bedding had to be done under the locomotive as I can testify from painful memories of lacerated knuckles caused by the inadequate clearance.

When wheels had to come out completely for journal turning or the six-monthly examination of crank axles for fractures, the locomotive was placed under a sheerleg of 35 tons capacity outside the shed and one end lifted high enough for the defective pair of wheels to be rolled out. These were then rolled into the machine shop for turning in the wheel lathe, using the drop table as a convenient means of rotating them through a quarter turn and on to a pair of temporary rails leading into the shop.

I became acquainted with a number of Robinson specialities, such as the Intensifore hydraulic cylinder lubricator, the Reliostop automatic train brake and his patent superheater header discharge valve – 'The sahnd wot makes the 'orses jump!' as I once heard an inspector describe its action!

Late in the summer of 1927 I was to spend two months with the boilersmiths under the supervision of John Brown, the leading boilersmith, an old Crewe man who had served his apprenticeship under Francis Webb at the time some experimental boilers were being constructed with water grates and water jacketed ashpans in an attempt to increase evaporation. J. B. related to me how he had been severely rebuked by his foreman for his temerity in opining that neither of these devices would work. Subsequent experience proved him right – icicles were seen hanging from the underside of the water jacketed ashpans in frosty weather whilst the joints of the water grates required constant attention. Under J. B.'s guidance I learned how to expand and bead boiler tubes, fuller seams, and later on was initiated into the highly-skilled art of detecting and drilling out broken copper stays. I was also allowed to try my hand at re-rivetting stay heads and like most beginners with the rivetting hammer, I left my trademark by indenting the plates with a few half-moons and crow's feet.

During that autumn of 1927 I spent six weeks with the hydraulic fitters at Marylebone goods warehouse, off Lisson Grove, then the largest building of its kind under one roof in London.

At the warehouse hydraulic power at a pressure of 750 lb/sq in was generated by two splendid twin-cylinder horizontal steam engines fitted with double slide valves on the Meyer principle. These engines were fed with steam from a battery of five Lancashire boilers, and were under constant load. It was an impressive sight to watch them start and see the great heavily-weighted hydraulic accumulators (themselves resembling up-ended Lancashire boilers) rise at each laboured stroke of the piston. Hydraulic power was fed to over 60 capstans distributed throughout the goods yard as well as to numerous hydraulic cranes and hoists in the warehouse itself. The motors of these capstans, made by Tannet Walker of Leeds, closely resembled miniature inside cylinder locomotives turned on their sides, the capstan head being affixed to the vertical two-throw crank shaft where a driving wheel would be in a locomotive.

My job was to reface the slide valves of these machines, which had to be a perfect fit to withstand such a high pressure as 750 lb/sq in. I was warned never to search for leaks with a naked hand, as even a pin-hole size jet would penetrate the flesh at that pressure. I helped as well to overhaul the mountings of one of the Lancashire boilers and learned the necessity of keeping the bronze fittings under lock and key as a precaution against brass thieves.

Early in November 1927 Mr Robinson sent for me and told me that I was to be transferred to King's Cross from the following Monday, in order to widen my experience. After thanking him for the excellent training I had received I left Neasden and the Great Central for the time being.

CHAPTER 5

FITTER

Early one wet November morning in 1927, I reported for duty at King's Cross Top Shed and my impressions as I trudged up the granite paved roadway through the goods yard can be briefly summarised – compared with the *fin-de-siècle* atmosphere of the Great Central at Marylebone, the Great Northern buildings at King's Cross were definitely mid-nineteenth century! There could be no doubt as to the identity of the plain yellow brick buildings, not unpleasing in appearance, seen on entering GN territory, for there was throughout a uniform style in the architecture of passenger terminus, granary, goods warehouses, offices, stables and locomotive depot.

The locomotive depot, or Top Shed as it was commonly known, was tucked away in a corner of the extensive goods yard, bounded on the west by the Regent's Canal and Midland Railway from St Pancras and to the north by the viaduct carrying the North London Railway across the GN main line at Belle Isle, between the Gas Works and Copenhagen tunnels; only from this viaduct could a comprehensive view of the depot be obtained.

Little could have changed since the fan shaped layout of the gaslit locomotive repair shop with its hand-operated overhead travelling crane, row of smiths forges and its machine shop powered by a beam engine (reputed then to be 120 years old, purchased with other property in Agar Town in 1852) was built: it would have been no surprise to have come upon a Sturrock or a Stirling Single!

Such nostalgic musings were promptly dispelled by Joe Ede the Foreman Fitter, who immediately put me to work assisting to equip the fleet of N2 suburban tank engines with tripcocks for working over the Metropolitan Railway 'Widened Lines' into Moorgate. The Metropolitan tanks were all stabled in the 'Derby' round shed, built for the accommodation of the Midland company's locomotives before the opening of its own line into St Pancras in 1868. It was in one of the stalls radiating from the 45ft turntable of this shed that the work of fitting the tripcock gear was carried out.

Round or half-round sheds, almost universal on the Continent and in America, have one great advantage over the through or dead end type – no time-consuming shed marshalling is required, but they are wasteful of space and present problems where the turntable is too short to accommodate a pug or four-wheel shunter to propel a dead engine off the turntable into its stall. Normally locomotives were left after throwing-out fires, raking out ashpans, and emptying smokeboxes, with enough steam to move off the turntable into their stall. When they had not, they were pumped up and down the Straw road in reverse gear until sufficient air pressure had been built up in the boiler to enable them to move off the turntable, a somewhat uncertain and hazardous operation depending as it did on a timely and energetic application of the hand brake – it was also most detrimental to the valves and piston packings from the dust and soot sucked down the blastpipe into the cylinders.

At one time there had been a glazed cupola over the turntable, but this had long since disappeared and it was now open to the elements. In winter heavy torrents from broken or choked rainwater pipes added to the general discomfort. The one bright spot was the cheerful glow from the sand-drying and firelighting furnace round which men were apt to congregate until sent about their business by G. B. Hennessey, the Assistant District Locomotive Superintendent, and Joe Ede in the course of their rounds of surveillance.

The round shed fitters, mostly engaged on valve and piston examination of the Metropolitan tanks (two days for a piston valve N2, one day for a slide valve N1 or Humpy) were a good-natured, cheerful lot who got stuck into their work, and when completed still found time to indulge in a game of quoits with discarded piston rings, using the buffers of an engine diametrically opposite as their targets.

There was at that time no officially recognised tea break, but needless to say one was taken despite the efforts of those in authority to suppress the practice. The wind of change was beginning to blow even in those far-off days, and it was a great concession for smoking to be permitted in the running shed for one hour daily, between 3.00pm and 4.00pm!

Authority to us meant bowler hats, long black mackintoshes

and highly polished leather leggings in the figures of Joe Ede, the foreman fitter, J. F. Sparke, the District Locomotive Superintendent, and his assistant G. B. (Mike) Hennessey. J. F. Sparke, a tall dignified man with a heavy cavalry moustache who occupied a company house off the Caledonian Road, we saw but seldom as he went about the district, but not so Mike Hennessey who was responsible for the day-to-day running of the principal shed and who was on call for all main line breakdowns. Mike Hennessey was a tall dark Irishman who had learned his trade at the famous Thames Iron Works, and lived with his family in a company house sandwiched between the fitting shop and the Midland Railway, accessible only through the goods yard. Generations of Assistant Locomotive Superintendents lived in that house until it was vacated by Bernard Adkinson in 1941, through blast damage from enemy bombing. In Victorian times it was customary for a railway supervisor to live on the job in order that emergencies such as breakdowns and accidents could be dealt with as speedily as possible. The need to live on the premises finally disppeared when the possession of a telephone in a private house and speedy transport either by car or tube became commonplace. A further advantage of living some distance away was that of no longer being consulted on trivial matters well within the competence of the shift supervisors.

After spending two or three weeks doing nothing but cutting and screwing vacuum train pipes and ratchet drilling $^{13}/_{16}$in diameter holes in pony truck radial arms for the attachment of the tripcocks, I decided that the extension of my running shed experience in that direction had proceeded far enough and I pressed Joe Ede for more general experience. To this request he acceded and I recall spending a few days with the hydraulic fitters, noting that the GN capstan engines differed from those of the Great Central in being three-cylinder radial engines, presumably giving a more even torque. Soon afterwards I spent about five or six weeks on boiler repairs under the superintendence of Jimmy Higgs, the foreman boilersmith.

I recall watching with admiration Roger Massingham and Horace Bussey (both M&GN men from Melton Constable) shape and fit a copper mouthpiece patch to the firehole of a large Atlantic. First of all the defective area with its attendant stays and rivets was cut out and the plate edges pared neatly to a feather edge. Next the $^{5}/_{8}$in thick copper patch was annealed and shaped to cover the area cut out leaving a considerable margin to take in the first row of copper stays. A hole was drilled between each stay for a conical headed copper set-screw, and finally the patch and steel door plate were rivetted together. In new construction such a joint would be made with a hydraulic rivetter, so ensuring that the rivets fitted the holes tightly, also that the plates were pressed closely together, whereas with ordinary hand rivetting there was a tendency for the rivet shank to shrink as it cooled and loosen in the plate. The technique adopted by these two skilled men was for each to use a heavy rivetting hammer, striking in unison, instead of holding up a heavy hammer against the rivet head to absorb the blow. The success of this technique obviously depended on perfect timing, and therein lay their greatest skill.

In 1927 King's Cross Top Shed was still very much 'Great Northern' and its claim to be its premier depot, if not supported by other contenders, certainly demonstrated a strong *esprit de corps*. More than most the old GN appeared to subscribe to the philosophy that railways run best on a judicious mixture of good beer and bad language! My old friend Ron Garraway, a true blue Great Eastern man, aptly summed up GN philosophy as one of 'Slap, bang, push and drive!'

The climax of my running shed experience occurred early in 1928 when to my delight I received a letter from Mr Sparke enclosing an engine pass together with a carefully thought-out programme of four weeks' footplate training, as shown by the following specimen:

Premium Apprentice D. W. Harvey
King's Cross

FOOTPLATE EXPERIENCE
Suburban Service
w/e 28.1.1928

	Diagram No.	Depart Shed a.m.	Engine No.	Driver
Monday	44	7.10	2642	C. Smither
Tuesday	45	6.00	2663	J. Williams
Wednesday	47	6.40	4762	H. Rogers
Thursday	55	6.12	4758	C. Waite
Friday	58	6.40	4608	W. Sellwood
Saturday	67	7.05	2647	W. Meakin

The round shed as seen from the footplate of a brand-new Beardmore-built N7 0–6–2T presented quite a different aspect as we rolled off the turntable to couple to two other light engines, all but one bound for the same destination, Alexandra Palace. The locomotive for High Barnet was detached at Highgate, while the remainder proceeded round the corner at Park Junction to the terminus at Alexandra Palace where they attached to their respective trains, already filling with City-bound passengers. I soon discovered that the fire of a locomotive working a train burns with a much more intense heat and requires more frequent feeding to maintain a good head of steam than does a light engine on a trial trip.

The descent through the tunnels from York Road to Moorgate ('down the rat hole') was an unforgettable experience, for here we were compelled by law 'to condense our own steam and consume our own smoke.' This was enforced by the City authorities' smoke inspectors posted at strategic points, who recorded the numbers of offending locomotives with a view to prosecution. On leaving York Road the jet or blower was put hard on and the condenser valve in the blastpipe closed, so turning the exhaust steam into the side tanks, where as it condensed it made the water bubble and crackle until it became so hot that condensation ceased and clouds of steam escaped from the vent pipes in front of the cab windows, filling the cab with wet steam mingled with the hot acrid fumes from the chimney.

At Moorgate the tanks were refilled with cold water in order that the injectors could work properly on the return journey to Alexandra Palace, which was uphill all the way. The conditions in the cab as we climbed through the tunnel up the 1 in 37 gradient to No 16 platform at King's Cross resembled those of a turkish bath! By comparison, the air we gulped in on bursting out of the tunnel seemed like pure ozone. On leaving the main line at Finsbury Park we began to climb in earnest and this required the hand brake to be screwed on hard at every stop in order to prevent the train rolling back as the vacuum brake was released. The sylvan surroundings of Highgate Woods and the spectacular view of London as seen from the viaduct at Muswell Hill came as a welcome respite after the inferno of the tunnels on the Metropolitan section.

During the week I spent on the Mets I went to other destinations on the Northern Heights, like High Barnet, Potters

Bar and Hertford, and usually did another stint with the afternoon shift before my thirst for footplating was slaked for one day.

Frequent visitors to all these destinations were the venerable North London Railway outside-cylinder four-coupled tank engines to be seen labouring up the banks with their trains of antique, four-wheeled close-coupled stock terminating in a birdcage observatory for the guard – real 1880s period pieces. These North London locomotives were always referred to as the Cockneys and for some obscure reason were supposed to have been built in Germany; as King's Cross men then used to work into Cannon Street, it is just possible that they may have confused them with the Borsig-built locomotives of the SE&CR.

Then followed a week on express goods trains leaving King's Cross during the late afternoon and returning from Peterborough early the following morning. These trains were all hauled by the three-cylinder K3s, exceptionally free-steaming locomotives thanks to the 6ft 0in diameter boiler, short tubes and long firebox. I found its firehole just the right height and had no difficulty in making the locomotive blow-off when challenged to do so by the regular fireman, who would cover the pressure gauge with his cap. The firing technique was to keep the back corners of the grate well packed, and not to fire more than half way down the sides, for vibration would do the rest, as the K3s were notoriously hard-riding despite their large axleboxes. Over the years I have found that rough-riding locomotives generally steamed well, possibly because the vibration shook the ash and cinders out of the fire and kept the air spaces clear – also possibly because the steam bubbles detached themselves more easily from the plates.

My training schedule for the final fortnight was on Pacifics working express passenger trains between London and Grantham with such well known top-link drivers as Ben Glasgow, Albert Pibworth and William Prior. The latter's regular locomotive was No 2545 *Diamond Jubilee* which like most of the Pacifics of that period still retained its original short-travel valve gear and 180 lb/sq in boiler.

I soon found that firing a wide firebox demanded quite a different technique from that required for a narrow box; the secret of success was to keep the back corners well packed up so that these fed the rest of the grate. The technique for stoking the back corners of a locomotive with a wide grate when firing through the narrow opening of the LNER trap type firebox, as developed over the years by GN firemen, was to swing the shovel blade in an arc right through the firehole, dropping at the same instant the front or guiding hand and finishing with a smart flick of the wrist of the other hand, so tipping the coal into the corner. Needless to say the metal shank of the shovel soon became too hot to handle unless a cloth or glove were used on the guiding hand, while blistered knuckles on the propelling hand was the penalty for any lack of smartness in withdrawing the blade!

I did have one trip on No 2555 *Centenary*, the first Pacific to have the redesigned valve gear and recorded that a pressure of 150 lb/sq in was maintained in the steamchest with a cut-off of 20 per cent and only 160 lb/sq in in the boiler – due no doubt to my lack of expertise!

A day that stands out in my memory is 8 February 1928, when after firing No 2545 to Grantham I went forward to Doncaster on No 2195, one of Sir Vincent Raven's handsome three-cylinder NER Atlantics. This I found very difficult to fire on account of its long narrow firebox, the canopy ('fish and chip oven') over the firehole, and its narrow cramped footplate which seemed to abound in projections on which I barked my knuckles!

The return journey from Doncaster was made on No 5511 *Marne*, a GCR Director class locomotive. This was my first experience of firing a Great Central locomotive and I found its high firehole and appetite for coal rather tiring after my morning's exertions. Fortunately No 5511 rode and steamed well and I was very favourably impressed by the well planned layout of the cab and boiler mountings, which was uniform on all Great Central types. By dint of strenuous efforts in ladling coal into the firebox I was able to keep the needle of the pressure gauge near the red mark; my surprise on looking into the firebox and seeing cinders dancing on the grate at the front can well be imagined. No 5511 came off at Grantham to be replaced by a Pacific No 2554 *Woolwinder*. We were warned by the stationmaster that HRH the Duke of York, who had that day been hunting with the Belvoir, was aboard – accordingly I left the management of the fire to the regular fireman. We arrived at King's Cross two minutes early and Gresley himself came up to speak to the driver.

The last week of my footplate experience was spent on the afternoon expresses and on two occasions I had the good fortune to accompany Bill Barnes on his regular locomotive No 4436, a large Atlantic with which he used to work the six-car West Riding

Pullman Limited. His best run was achieved with No 4450 when attempting to recoup a delay of 17 minutes by covering the 76½ miles from Peterborough to King's Cross in 68 minutes. The 27 miles between Huntingdon and Hitchen took only 20 minutes, an average speed of 81mph. My principal recollection of these trips was the abundance of steam, the cracking exhaust when climbing through the many tunnels and the dazzling white heat from the firehole. There was no need for a pyrometer on these engines – the seat of the fireman's pants told him all he needed to know about the degree of superheat! I found the Atlantic easy to fire once one had become accustomed to the characteristic tail wag which helped to bring the coal forward to within easy reach of the shovel on the somewhat cramped footplate.

Two Ivatt refinements found on the Atlantics and perpetuated by Gresley on his own locomotives were the vacuum-operated band brake on the reversing shaft to stop the lever from vibrating and rattling, and a fine tooth reversing quadrant to permit notching up with precision, although advantage was seldom taken of this.

Much to my regret I received a letter from Mr Sparke on 17 February informing me that my request for an extension of time in the running department had been turned down and I was to report back to Doncaster Works on the following Monday.

Many changes had taken place in the plant during my nine months' absence. Francis Wintour had retired from the post of Assistant Mechanical Engineer, Southern Area. He was replaced by Robert A. Thom, a rotund little Scotsman, a boilermaker by trade who had at one time been in charge of the locomotive department of the Lancashire, Derbyshire & East Coast Railway before it was absorbed by the Great Central. Peter Stewart, the foreman in charge of the boilershop, (identifiable by his *Daily Mail* pattern hard felt hat then much in vogue) had retired, to be replaced by Foreman Hudson from Gorton. Foreman Treece of the top turnery had gone also. Plans were in hand to turn the old erecting shop into a large new machine shop by filling-in the traverser pit and transferring some of the machinery from the upper turnery, which was to become a vast drawing office accommodating all locomotive, carriage, wagon and outdoor machinery draughtsmen under one roof. Ex-LD&ECR locomotives began to arrive in the Crimpsall for general repairs on the closure of its Tuxford works, in the shape of Kitson-built

0–6–2 and 0–6–4 tanks as well as some small Manning Wardle saddle tanks belonging to the East & West Yorkshire Union Railway that had been absorbed by the LNER.

Boilers began to arrive from Gorton for cutting-up, as this operation could be carried out more cheaply at Doncaster. The few weeks remaining before the expiry of my apprenticeship in April were spent at the old engine weighhouse which once stood where the lawn and British Rail Engineering sign is now; here at least I was working on locomotives in steam.

On the completion of my apprenticeship F. H. Eggleshaw sent for me and told me that I was being retained in the service. He stated that he had a job that I could do for him in costing the production of copper stays, adding dryly that I was 'not to go around telling all and sundry that I had got Mr Gresley's job!' At the same time he reminded me that I was on the books as a fitter and when visitors were around I should wear overalls. I found this and other costing exercises most instructive and of great value in demonstrating how difficult it is to justify (for instance) the installation of a new and costly machine to replace ancient but still serviceable machinery operated by apprentices on low wages. There were, for example, in the brass shop three old lathes built by Joseph Whitworth in 1847 that had come from the temporary works at Boston – these survived until the dismantling of the turnery.

I do not wish to give the impression that there were none but old machines in the plant. On the contrary, Doncaster was at the forefront in having some of the best and most modern British and American machine tools available. The yardstick for replacement was a saving of ten per cent of the capital cost of the machine in its first year of operation. This was no hypothetical target, but one that was expected to be achieved in practice and woe betide the estimator if it was not!

Another job for Mr Thom that came my way was to measure up and make drawings where none existed of stationery boilers, with details of any patches that had been applied. One that I recall was for the boiler of a steam dredger belonging to the South Yorkshire Navigation, sometimes referred to as 'Sir Sam Fay's Navy' or the 'Meccano Dreadnought!'

An incident that left a lasting impression on my mind was to see resting on a side table in the Works Manager's office a heavy (as I thought) 2 to 1 valve motion beam which normally took two men to lift, picked up by Arthur Boulby the bandy-legged shop labourer and carried out on his shoulder! Seeing my astonishment Mr Eggleshaw volunteered the information that it was made of a new, light, extremely strong material called Duralamin and that it was being fitted experimentally to a K3 class locomotive together with valve heads of the same material. If successful it would, by reducing the inertia forces, overcome the problem of the middle valve over-running at high speeds. Unfortunately this experiment, like the chromium plating of valve heads and liners of Norwich K3 Nos 1970 and 1973 twenty years later was not a success for the same reason, scuffing away of the rubbing surfaces. This same combination of materials is very successful in diesel practice with forced feed and splash lubrication and I can only conclude that its lack of success when applied to a steam locomotive is due to intermittent lubrication caused by condensate washing off the lubricant and by sucking in ash and hot smokebox gases when coasting.

Another recollection of this period is a visit to Neville Hill depot, where I saw stripped down for inspection a D49 Shire class locomotive equipped with Lentz poppet valves operated from the normal Walshaerts valve motion by means of an oscillating camshaft. I recall the District Locomotive Superintendent extolling the merits of these valves for remaining steam-tight for periods far in excess of what was obtainable with piston valves, even those with the new, narrow rings.

Shortly after being admitted as a Graduate of the Institution of Locomotive Engineers I was called upon to fill a vacancy for a progress man in the boiler shop. My job was to produce an accurate weekly forecast of the completion date of all boilers under repair and on hand and to allocate these to locomotives coming into the works for general repairs. Repair schedules were tightened, and there was much chasing of material in order to try and achieve target times ranging from six days for the general repair of a saddle tank to twenty-one days for a Pacific. This often involved not only a change of boiler but a change of wheels and sometimes motion as well.

The depression or slump was now beginning to bite and this coupled with increasing road competition brought the finances of the railway companies to such a state that a 2½ per cent levy on all salaries and wages was accepted by the staff on the understanding the 1¼ per cent would be restored when the fortunes of the railways improved, which in the event took nearly nine years!

As the months went by I came to realise that I could never be really happy in a production job in the plant, so when a vacancy occurred for a fitter at Doncaster Carr Sheds, I applied and was accepted. Some said that I was a fool to go back to overalls but I have never regretted having done so. On the contrary, those five or six years earning my living with my hands was of the utmost benefit to me throughout my career. I had not been working long at the Carr Sheds before the essential difference between repairing a running locomotive and one that was stopped was brought home to me. I learned the hard way not to start pulling one to pieces before first finding out at what time it and those behind it were booked out.

All repairs booked by drivers were transcribed by the timekeepers on to separate repair slips. These were distributed by the foreman fitter who allocated the work according to a man's skill and what work he had already. As a newly-fledged fitter my bundle of repair slips contained a high proportion of 'Sands making to run' 'Glands to repack' or 'Injectors to clean out'. The problem came at the end of the day when each slip had to be returned to the foreman, duly signed and the time spent on each job recorded. Often the aggregate amount of work far exceeded eight hours if carried out thoroughly and conscientiously. The alternatives were either to return them as not done, at the risk of being considered slow and inefficient, or whether after taking a look at the job, one could safely sign them off as done, as many did – not a few piston glands have been repacked by the application of a little cylinder oil to the rod! This aspect of running repairs was always worrying and the problem was not solved until after World War II when a system of standard examinations was introduced. It then became permissible after inspection to defer minor repairs until the next shed day, when a systematic examination of the locomotive in steam was made and all booked defects dealt with.

Early in 1930 a vacancy occurred for a fitter at King's Cross and I decided to apply as prospects of promotion were distinctly bleak, and if I was to spend several years at the bench then it would be much more pleasant to do so where I could live at home.

On leaving Doncaster George Oakes gave me his blessing and I began for the second time to make that now familiar journey over the Regent's Canal and through the goods yard to the Top Shed. Joe Ede, the foreman fitter who addressed everyone as 'Jack' greeted me thus: 'Well, Jack, have you come back to be a good boy or a bloody noosance?' To this I retorted 'That depends entirely on what you make me, Joe!'

As at Doncaster, I found that there had been changes during my absence. Several old faces had gone, including Mike Hennessey, to be replaced by men made redundant at other depots, some of whom laboured under a sense of grievance – consequently the atmosphere was less happy than it had been. Material changes were being made too, the old overhead travelling hand crane was being replaced by a new Royce 30 ton electric crane. An electrically-operated wheel drop was being installed to supplement the old hydraulic drop table operated by Uncle Smith, a little gnome of a man with large diamond shaped ears, who hailed from Longhedge Works on the Chatham. Electric lighting was being installed to replace gas lighting and electric motors were soon to displace the old beam engine bought in 1852 for £356 from Worsam & Company, with other property in Agar Town at the time the top shed was being built. This did indeed mark the end of an era; no more would its flywheel have to be barred off a dead centre to enable it to be started with the hand gear; nor would we have to dash frantically into the engine room to stop the engine galloping when its governor belt came off.

The following year I was given the job to finish the dismantling of this venerable engine, reputed to be 120 years old, for re-erection in the Railway Museum at York. The balance beam and four supporting columns had already been taken down and I was to take apart the four segments comprising the heavy cast-iron flywheel so that it and the crankshaft could be lifted out. The lower half of this 14ft 6in flywheel was sunk in a deep narrow pit while the upper half was encased in a kind of cupboard in the wall next to the machine shop. The operation was to burn off the wrought-iron hoops encircling the flywheel boss, to separate the upper from the lower half wheel, secured by dowels and cotters and to lift these out with the aid of chain blocks and rollers. I particularly remember this job, for when splitting the nuts of the air pump foundation bolts my mate, a young and inexperienced engine cleaner, missed completely the chisel bar I was holding and brought the 7 lb hammer down on my wrist, entailing a visit to the hospital and three weeks off duty with my arm in a sling!

In the hard times of the early 1930s falling traffic receipts were matched by a corresponding reduction in the number of men

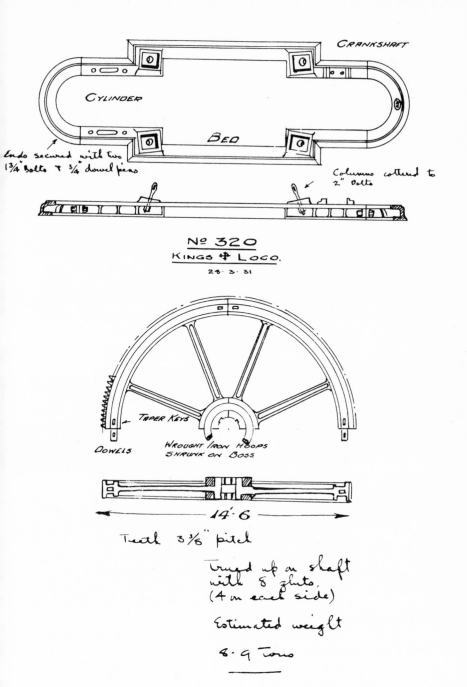

CRANKSHAFT

CYLINDER

BED

Ends secured with two
1¾" Bolts & ¾" dowel pins

Columns cottered to
2" Bolts

No 320
KINGS ⚓ LOCO.
28. 3. 31

TAPER KEYS

DOWELS

WROUGHT IRON HOOPS
SHRUNK ON BOSS

14'. 6

Teeth 3⅛" pitch

Trued up on shaft
with 8 struts.
(4 on each side)

Estimated weight

8. 9 Tons

Beam engine, Kings Cross Loco. Sketches of bed and flywheel.

employed and hours worked. Labourers, cleaners and junior mates were discharged while many drivers were put back to firing and firemen to cleaning. Sunday duty and overtime was severely curtailed. In the 18 months that I was at King's Cross I had but two Sundays' work and these were short turns of eight hours, whereas the older and married men usually worked from 6.00am to 6.00pm. The posting of the Sunday duty list (which Joe Ede wisely left to the latest possible moment) would be greeted with ironic cheers, raspberries and on one occasion by the singing of the then popular song 'Happy Days are Here Again!'

During the slump there was, as a result of these economy measures, a general shortage of mates and labourers and it became common for two young fitters to work together and for much more hand fitting to be done. For example, when dealing with a hot axlebox, the axle journal had to be very deeply scored indeed before it was considered bad enough to put in the lathe for turning, owing to the difficulty in mustering enough men to operate the travelling hand crane. In consequence we became skilled at filing journals round to calipers and then polishing them with sheets of emery cloth wrapped round a length of discarded carriage dynamo belting, applied to the journal and pulled to and fro. When an especially good job was required we finished off by burnishing the journal with iron wire gauze (then the standard jointing material) and oil. We also became expert at hand fitting axleboxes with file and scraper, in which we were greatly assisted by the skill of the whitesmith who would wipe off surplus white metal while it was still plastic, with a length of broom handle smeared with tallow. Worn big-end brasses too were closed by chipping and filing as often as not. In skilled hands the chisel can become a precision instrument.

I had a good variety of jobs covering most aspects of running shed work, including my fair share of smokeboxes. I was initiated into the system of carrying out examinations piecemeal between trips that King's Cross had brought to a fine art. For example, a locomotive would have one piston examined, de-carbonised and re-ringed one day, the other side on the next and possibly the valves on the third day. By so doing it was legitimately shown as at work, and this enabled King's Cross to maintain an exceptionally low stop list.

In order to save time at valve and piston examinations, piston valves when extracted were taken into the shop for attention by a specialist bench fitter, thus leaving the fitters free to carry on with the examination of the pistons. One fitter's method of de-carbonising the narrow multi-ring valve heads which were then coming into vogue, was to heat them to a dull red heat in a smith's forge, so releasing the rings gummed solid in their grooves. These narrow ring valves proved very difficult to extract from their sleeves when carbon accumulating under the rings prevented these from contracting. When this happened as it often did there was nothing for it but to dismantle the valve motion and by placing a bottle jack against the motion plate to jack out the reluctant valve. On one occasion when faced with this predicament with a Class K3 2–6–0, we consulted Joe Ede, who rashly decided to take a short cut and pull the valve out with a shunting engine using a chain to unite the two. The first tug broke off the shunter's lamp iron to which the chain was attached, the second broke the chain and bent the valve spindle while the third, after knotting together the two pieces of broken chain, pulled the boss out of the back valve head, leaving its rim behind and firmly wedged in the front sleeve! This was laboriously cut out with a long round-nose chisel and 4 lb hammer! Ultimately this difficulty was overcome by boring out the front valve sleeve slightly larger than the back one, thus allowing the back head to pass through easily.

It was about this time that the old Derby round shed and adjacent messroom (the original MR offices and workshop) was literally pulled down after the brickwork had been demolished by two locomotives, an N1 and a J52 placed about 45° apart and connected by long chains to two of the columns supporting the heavy cast-iron ring above the turntable. It came down with a tremendous crash, fortunately without damage to the turntable, which had been securely packed and protected by sleepers. After the debris had been cleared both turntable and pits continued in use until the former carriage shop became the home of the Metropolitan tanks on the departure of the Carriage and Wagon Department to new premises at Highgate.

While enjoying my work as a fitter I was becoming increasingly anxious as to my future prospects. The upshot was that I sought and obtained an interview with W. G. P. Maclure, the Locomotive Running Superintendent at Liverpool Street on 13 February 1931. That interview I regard as the turning point of my career. It transpired that a copy of the Apprentices' Training Committee Minutes was missing from my personal file and while this was being sought, Mr Maclure questioned me generally about my knowledge of locomotives. Eventually the missing papers were produced and I shall never forget how his face brightened as he exclaimed 'Why, you have an excellent record; I am afraid that you have been overlooked!'. He went on to say that there were no vacancies at the moment and that he would be retiring at the end of the month, but he would make sure that I was not overlooked by his successor, S. W. Groom. He was as good as his word for exactly a month later I was sent for by Mr Groom and in three months, as a result of that interview, received a letter promoting me to Mechanical Chargeman at the little GN shed at Belgrave Road, Leicester.

CHAPTER 6

MECHANICAL CHARGEMAN

The supervision of a small shed like Belgrave Road, Leicester was excellent training for a youngster and it was with great pride and eagerness that I started my new duties as Mechanical Chargeman or working foreman responsible for the maintenance of six tender engines and a total staff of 20. Hitherto I had been accustomed to taking orders, now for the first time in my life I had to give them to men, some old enough to be my father. Would they obey me? I need not have worried, for the tradition of discipline was such that my instructions were generally accepted without dispute. I soon found that I had no shortage of elderly advisers in the three brothers Goddard, all anxious to keep the young 'Coddy' (Leicestershire for 'gaffer') right!

My domain comprised a well-built brick dead-end shed, accommodating six tender engines on three roads, all with full length pits with washout hydrants in between. A well-appointed oil store with overhead storage tanks delivering into calibrated measuring glasses occupied one corner of the building, then came the signing-on lobby with an archway leading into the shed and at the opposite corner my office, its window overlooking the 45ft turntable.

Also within view of my office window was a massive brick built coaling stage, supporting a 56,000-gallon water storage tank, with ashpit below. It may well be asked how the continued existence of such lavish accommodation could be justified for so few locomotives, with the much larger Great Central depot at Braunstone Gate only two miles away on the other side of the city. The answer was that by rail the two depots were over 60 miles apart and as the facilities were there, these might just as well be used. For the purposes of manning and administration Belgrave Road depot came under the supervision of Roland Bardsley the Depot Superintendent at the Great Central Shed. Later on when I went to the GE section on promotion I was to discover that all that was really necessary to maintain so few locomotives was a pit, a hydrant, a wagon of coal and an old coach body combining the functions of office, fitting shop, store and messroom – then did Belgrave Road indeed seem like a Paradise Lost!

The extension to Leicester was built during the expansionist period of the GNR, which with the LNWR built a joint line connecting their two systems at Bottisford and Market Harborough respectively. Unfortuntely for the GN its handsome red-brick passenger terminus facing Belgrave Road, with provision for four roads under an all-over vaulted roof, did not fulfil its early promise and when I went to Leicester in 1931 only two platforms were in use, the other half of the station being boarded up. The adjacent and commodious goods warehouse with two floors always seemed full of bales and other commodities when I made my periodic visits to examine its lifting appliances. I tried so to organise my work that the mornings were spent in overalls working either on my locomotives or inspecting the Goods Warehouse machinery that entailed examining link by link the four granary hoist chains, each 90ft long, and testing the spring-loaded safety devices of the lift cages, which in the event of a suspension cable breaking would fly out and dig into the wooden runners, so arresting the cages descent. If all went well the afternoon was spent in the office on paper work.

My locomotive stock comprised three Ivatt Class D3 4–4–0, passenger engines with short fireboxes, Nos 4309, 4315, 4318, and three six-coupled goods engines Class J6 No 3521, J3 No 3396, and J11 No 5234. In addition to all running repairs, I undertook the periodical examinations of these locomotives.

The trains worked by Belgrave Road were as follows: the 6.00am and 2.30pm Goods Yard pilots; then came the 7.10am passenger train to Grantham, double-headed as far as John O'Gaunt, where the second locomotive was detached in order to bring city workers into Leicester before working the 9.00am Grantham. The last passenger train of the day was the 6.10pm Lowesby and back, consisting of two coaches and worked by the locomotive prepared for the 8.25pm Newark goods, our only freight turn.

There were no Sunday trains during the winter months and I went home most weekends travelling by the Midland route in preference to the Great Central as Saint Pancras was more convenient for me than Marylebone. A regular travelling companion on the journey back to Leicester on Sunday evenings was a young man then serving his apprenticeship at Derby and like me a keen modelmaker, Ron Jarvis, who in years to come would occupy a leading position on the design staff of British Railways and achieve distinction by his competent rebuilding of the SR Merchant Navy class. One Saturday morning my plans for the weekend were disrupted by the surprising news that a private-owner wooden wagon loaded with potatoes had been broken in two during shunting operations in the goods yard. On inspection I found this to be true. It had broken at the weakest point in the wooden solebars below the door opening where these were morticed to receive the cross-members. The two broken ends, 50yd apart, were inclined downwards and resting on the rails, while the intervening space was strewn with sacks of potatoes. A screw jack and a platelayers trolley soon made the longer end mobile while a scratch tug-of-war team with a wagon rope quickly pulled the short end clear of the track. According to my carriage and wagon examiner the reason for this wagon pulling apart was that it had not been fitted with through stay rods as required by the Railway Clearing House for wagons not fitted with continuous drawgear.

Sunday excursion trains to Skegness or Mablethorpe commenced running with the introduction of the summer timetable. No 296 in the yellow PST book (Programme of Standard Times) gave the running times for the 10.00am special to Skegness and No 298 those for the 10.10am special to Mablethorpe. The standard excursion train at that time consisted of two ex-London suburban close-coupled train sets. Each set comprised eleven four-wheeled compartment coaches seating six a side, with a birdcage observatory for the guard at each end, and no lavatory accommodation, as the condition of Sleaford Station platform on a Monday morning bore witness!

Twenty-two of these four-wheelers was near the limit of the haulage capacity of the short firebox D3s, but depending on the weather and the number of intending passengers an additional six-wheeler would be attached (equal to '23½'), no mean load for a small four-coupled engine over a hilly road. The technique when backing onto the train was to set back hard into the buffer stops in order to compress the train buffer springs, then to apply the brake. On receiving the 'Right away' the regulator was opened as the brake was released so that the energy stored in the buffer springs assisted in starting the train. With loads such as these it is not surprising that these little engines laboured up the back to the first stop at Humberston as if hauling coal trains. A record load of two 11-coach excursion sets plus three six-wheelers equal to '26½' was hauled on one occasion by a long firebox D2 4–4–0 sent from Colwick specially for this purpose and worked by Bert Dover, a driver from the Great Central shed.

It was difficult to gauge the number of intending passengers, as the tramcars bringing them to the station did not start running until shortly before train time. On one occasion, due to an oversight, Driver Jack Bithell booked to work the 10.00am Skegness had not been advised for duty, so while a cleaner possessing a motorcycle combination hurried off to collect him, Alf Goddard, my boiler washer and I prepared the locomotive, took it out and coupled it to the train, already full of passengers. The reason for the delay was explained to the passengers, who gave Bithell, the proud wearer of a fine pair of waxed moustachios a rousing cheer, as, seated in the motor cycle sidecar, he was driven alongside the train to the engine. A quick assurance that all was in order, a pop on the whistle and they were away!

As the reader will have gathered, Belgrave Road was a sleepy little place for most of the year, but it really did come to life during August week when Leicester made its annual exodus to the seaside. During the Friday night preceding this Bank holiday, those maids-of all-work on any British railway, six-coupled goods engines, mostly J6s and Pom Poms, coupled together in twos and threes began to arrive from Colwick, together with coaching stock. The first train of these John Brown guaranteed excursions left for Scarborough at 3.45am on the Saturday morning, then came others at short intervals to Cleethorpes, Yarmouth, Skegness and Mablethorpe. Every man on the shed who could be spared from other duties, myself included, helped to fill coal tubs or assisted Tom Goddard the coalman, in winding them up with the hand-coaling crane so that tenders could be topped up to capacity before departure. Most of the excitement was over by midday, only to be resumed the following morning and the day after until one began to wonder where all the people came from.

There was a memorable occasion during August week 1933 when on the Wednesday several hundred intending passengers were left behind after the booked trains to Skegness, all crammed to capacity, had left. The Station Master at the Great Central station came over to see what he could do: his offer to refund fares was declined – what the intending passengers wanted and intended to have was a train to take them to Skegness! A hasty consultation with various foremen followed, the yard was combed for rolling stock, and I offered the locomotive off the Goods Yard pilot if this could be spared until a replacement became available in two hours time. So a train of sorts was assembled, including two milk vans without seats, if the intending passengers were prepared to travel in them. This offer was accepted with alacrity and good humour, whereupon the crowd dragged the heavy benches off the platform into the milk vans to make their 96-mile journey a little less fatiguing. That evening the *Leicester Mercury* (which was flown by air daily to its readers at Skegness) contained the headline 'Leicester Travels to the Seaside in Milkvans!'

About once a week Roland Bardsley would make his routine visit of inspection and at longer intervals H. R. Silver who had succeeded J. W. Hulme as District Locomotive Superintendent at Colwick, would include Belgrave Road on his tour of inspection. On one of these visits the First Aid cabinet was inspected and I was asked whether I was a qualified First Aider and I had to answer 'No', whereupon he replied. 'Every supervisor should be qualified in first aid – find out where your local class is held and join!' This I did, and have since kept up that knowledge which has been of great benefit.

Towards the end of 1933 it was suggested to me by a friend on the Great Eastern that I should apply for a vacancy that would be occurring shortly for a mechanical chargeman at Brentwood, a small sub-shed hitherto under a driver-in-charge but now to be raised in status following on the quadrupling of the line to Shenfield and consequent increased traffic. I had been at Belgrave Road now for two-and-a-half years and throughout this time I had never had the opportunity of relieving in higher grade posts, a privilege enjoyed by my friends in the Stratford district. For this reason I decided to apply for the impending vacancy at Brentwood, even if there was no improvement in my status.

I was successful, and at the subsequent interview with S. W. Groom was informed that if I succeeded in pleasing Leslie Preston Parker, District Locomotive Superintendent at Stratford it would stand me in good stead in the future. On 28 December 1933 I reported at Stratford to Mr Parker, who on learning that I had worked on N2s at Kings Cross confided to me that for some reason or other those at Brentwood were always in trouble, 'but you will know all about N2s won't you, Harvey?' implying that by appointing me to Brentwood a transformation in their condition was expected! The importance of the new, augmented suburban service getting away to a good start was stressed. It was typical of Mr Parker that when I enquired at what hours he wished me to take duty, he replied 'I never tell my supervisors what hours they are to work but I shall expect you to be there when you are wanted.'

Wishing to make sure that all my locomotives, six N2s and Super Claud No 8791 were in steam in good time I took duty at midnight on New Year's eve 1934 and stayed there until the early afternoon, when I received a visit from L. P. Parker, who was touring his district to see how the new service was running.

Like all privileged to have been trained by LPP, I am proud to number myself as 'one of Mr Parker's young men'. At times we often thought him a hard and exacting taskmaster who expected too much from his pupils when entrusting them, for example, with such highly responsible jobs as relieving the regular running foreman at Liverpool Street on a foggy November evening during the rush hour. This, however, was LLP's way of finding out our capacity and capability. Those that survived their ordeal have good reason to be grateful to him, as the following extract from a letter written to me in his own hand, after I had left the LNER for Nigeria will show: 'As I told you before you sailed I have every confidence in your ability not only to give satisfaction in your present position but also to take full advantage of any opportunities that come your way. If I had been able to offer promotion in my own district to all the capable young men I have lost I should have by now the best run piece of a railway in this country or any other.'

The two road-shed at Brentwood was sited at the country end of the station behind the down platform, and at one time possessed a turntable as the semi-circular recess in the cutting retaining wall (which is still there) bears witness. At the end of the shed looking out on to the station yard was a small room that combined the functions of signing-on lobby, notice display and messroom; oil and material stores were kept in the tank house above the cutting. My office was a small, wooden contractors' hut about 5ft square in a corner of the shed, with neither heat nor light other than a paraffin hurricane lamp.

The N2 tanks that I had inherited, Nos 4722, 4723, 4726, 4737,

In this picture, Leslie Preston Parker is seated third from left in the front row.

LNER Class V2 No 4771 *Green Arrow*, now preserved, climbing Horsforth Bank on 17 September 1977. (*J. Aylard*)

Norwich motive power depot (*above*) *circa* 1880 and (*below*) in 1982

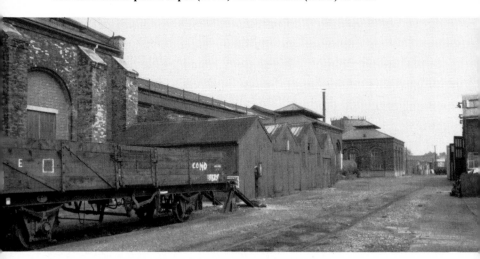

The original Yarmouth & Norwich Railway buildings at Norwich motive power depot.

890 and 891 were well past their prime. The last two were non-condensing and had seen prolonged service in Glasgow before coming south, and it came as no surprise that they were unpopular with the enginemen accustomed to the comfortable cabs of their Great Eastern N7s. In particular they disliked the faceplate or lifting injectors, due partly to unfamiliarity and partly to poor maintenance. As a result fires were being thrown out all over the line. Poor steaming due to blowing superheater element joints was another cause of failure.

A measure of their unreliability was the number of different locomotives figuring on the oil sheets that I had to compile every four weeks – had none failed this would not have exceeded seven (my allocation) plus the occasional pilot from Romford. During my first four weeks at Brentford no fewer than 29 different locomotives figured on this statement; no wonder that Mr Parker was gravely concerned! Blowing superheater element joints were a nightmare. Smokeboxes were not the pleasantest of places to work in at the best of times, and the twin-tube element of the Gresley top and bottom header superheater was particularly vulnerable to distortion and consequent leakage at its numerous copper joints. Experience since showed that copper was an unreliable jointing material for high degree superheat, and that is why designs such as the Robinson expanded and Melesco ball-ended element superseded the Schmidt copper gasket type. However, this knowledge was not of much immediate practical help – my job was to do my best with the limited facilities that I had available. I remember removing all 34 elements from No 4737 and annealing double that number of copper joints in the mess room fire, and how on water testing after replacement water still sprayed from those joints like the fountains in Trafalgar Square. I could have wept as copiously as they leaked! Ultimately I succeeded in getting them passably tight but it was an unsatisfactory job.

On the same locomotive I fitted a complete set (16) of new piston valve rings, laboriously reducing the thickness of each ring by filing to make it fit its groove, only to have the locomotive called into shops shortly afterwards. It was then as I trudged back to my lodgings in the evening after spending a solid eight hours fitting and another hour on paperwork in my sentry box of an office with my feet wrapped in a sack to keep out the cold, that I looked back on Belgrave Road as a Paradise Lost!

Spring was coming and I was just beginning to see some reward for my labours when L. P. Parker transferred me to Wood Street, Walthamstow, which shared with Enfield the distinction of operating the so-called Jazz service in and out of Liverpool Street, then the most intensively operated steam surburban service in the world and of necessity air braked.

All the original GER short-travel valve N7s with Belpaire boilers, duplex Ramsbottom safety valves and cast-iron parallel chimneys similar to those on the 1500s were allocated to the Jazz service during the 1930s. The 1000s went to Enfield and the 990s to Wood Street. The service ran like clockwork. There were fourteen locomotives to work thirteen diagrams, thus leaving one spare each day for washing-out and mechanical examination. In 1934 these were all doubled-manned. During the morning and evening peaks a train comprising two articulated quintuple sets left or arrived at Liverpool Street every two minutes. The Enfield trains used platforms 1 and 3 and the Chingford trains Nos 2 and 4, each departing at four-minute intervals. This was the shortest practicable time in which these crowded steam-hauled trains could be emptied of up to nine hundred passengers and refilled. The Cambridge line trains used the same tracks as far as Clapton Junction and the headway between trains as far as Hackney Downs, where the Enfield line diverged, could be as little as a minute-and-a-half. Rigorous punctuality was essential, and even a two- or three-minute late arrival of a locomotive into the carriage sidings to pick up its train would result in a complete round trip being cancelled rather than risk disorganising the punctual running of the remainder. This was especially the case at the start of the evening peak when trains were lengthened, half-trains being run during the slack period in the middle of the day. Two of the thirteen diagrams were treble-shifted (the Burglar turns). All the others were double turns, so in all 28 sets of drivers and firemen were required, rotating through one big link. In addition there was a passed fireman and a passed cleaner on each shift to cover sickness and emergencies; holiday relief was supplied from Stratford.

Wood Street possessed a well-built brick two-road running shed for washing-out and repairs, with ashpits outside. Two old carriage bodies, each sub-divided with internal partitions, served as office, fitting shop, notice room, signing-on lobby, and cleaners' mess.

Staff at Wood Street included a boiler washer (who often

worked single-handed if his mate was busy lifting ashes) and a fitter and his assistant who carried out the heavier periodical examinations. I did the lighter jobs such as injectors and Westinghouse brake examinations beside attending to any failures occurring at Chingford. I recall once changing a Westinghouse pump top head in 35 minutes, not bad going with everything scalding hot, especially if the steam cock was blowing through. The conditions then can be likened to lifting a kettle of fast boiling water, without a lid, off a stove. A fitter and mate were on duty from 6.00am to 2.00pm while I worked alternate weeks with the sub-shed chargeman, one week from 6.00am to 2.00pm and the next from 11.00am to 7.00pm.

A valve and piston examination was achieved in one day on an N7 by the following method. The fitter would have both piston valves out and de-carbonised by breakfast time, say 8.00am to 8.30am. These were then replaced, boxed-up and one side piston dealt with. A fitter and his mate sent from the crane shop at Stratford would then examine and replace the remaining piston during the afternoon, thus avoiding the need to call on Stratford for another locomotive.

As the locomotives were never turned but always faced chimney to country the flanges of the leading coupled wheels wore sharp much quicker than the remainder. These sharp edges (which if allowed to develop tended to split points) were removed from time to time by attaching a profiling tool to the brake hanger of the offending tyre and slowly moving the locomotive ahead, at the same time gently applying the hand brake to put on the feed. With such a primitive appliance, lacking in rigidity, the tool tended to dig in unless corrective action was taken quickly.

The Jazz service, being self-contained, was the only one that kept working without trouble during fog as both Wood Street and Enfield locomotives were then pooled. As only one train in four ran during fog, each depot accumulated a surplus. The headache came when fog working was lifted and one tried to get the locomotives back onto their right diagrams for changing-over at Liverpool Street.

I have mentioned that the Jazz service was Westinghouse braked – this continued right to the end of steam traction. Early trials with the vacuum brake soon after the 1923 Grouping condemned it as being too slow in releasing. The need for a rapid release will be appreciated when it is explained that in the working timetable, arrival and departure times were shown for only Bethnal Green, Hackney Downs and Wood Street, and at these only for 30 seconds. All the other stations had an average stopping time of 10–15 seconds.

With such a dynamic personality as L. P. Parker as ringmaster we were certainly left in no doubt that his was an enlightened and go-ahead administration. For example, in any large organisation that has been in existence for perhaps a hundred years a major difficulty arises in keeping an ever-changing staff acquainted with past instructions of which a written record no longer exists and is remembered only by the older men. LPP remedied this deficiency by supplying each of his shedmasters and supervisors with a ring file containing a set of standing orders, embodying these old instructions revised and edited by him, to which others were added from time to time. These proved invaluable to us as a guide to procedure, and woe betide the man who had not filed, indexed and made himself acquainted with the contents; as proof of their merit, LPP's system was still in use on the Eastern Region fifteen years after his death. I recall that M300 set out the procedure for setting valves, while S314 laid down that no trade union notice was to be put up before it had been scrutinised and signed by me – that led to some tussles as can be imagined! Another of LPP's innovation was his 'Review of the Condition of Passenger Engines', known by the staff at Stratford as the Book of Death.

It was essential that whoever was responsible for allocating locomotives to jobs should have an intimate knowledge of their condition. When the numbers were small this was easy enough, but at a large shed like Stratford that with its sub-sheds had as many locomotives as the Brighton Line (altogether 618) it was well beyond the capacity of the average memory. It was customary at large sheds for the Assistant Locomotive Superintendent to make the booking of express passenger engines his personal responsibility, leaving the allocation of the remainder to the running foremen. In order to reduce this problem of numbers to a manageable size, everything relating to motive power at Stratford had long been divided into two sections, the Tank side and the Tender side, each with its own running foremen and chargehands. This worked tolerably well but cases occurred, especially at holiday times, of some old crock breaking-down early in the day and disrupting the service. ('Put your best engines on the early trains and the worst on the last, then if it does break down only that train is delayed' was sound advice). LPP overcame this difficulty by making his inspectors ride on every passenger engine at least once a month. The steaming riding and general condition was noted on a master record held by the Chief Running Foreman – a tick in black signified good or satisfactory, one in blue, indifferent, and one in red, bad or rough.

In the case of poor steaming the foreman fitter and foreman boilersmith personally had to certify that every item of a long list of possible defects had been methodically checked. If necessary a water test and checking of chimney, blastpipe alignment and dimensions followed. Naturally such methodical methods did not meet with universal approval. Sometimes fitting staff would take short cuts and do some blind signing. If this was discovered they had caused to regret it, for I well recall Charlie Greenwood, the then foreman fitter expressing the opinion on emerging from a grilling in LLP's office that he would rather have his teeth extracted any day than undergo that ordeal again!

Sometimes when relieving at Stratford we would be summoned into the Presence to partake of tea (china) from his famous glass teapot. This was no social occasion, but an opportunity for him to find out what progress we had made in gaining knowledge. His gibe that 'An engineer who cannot use a slide rule, Harvey, is about of as much use as a fitter who cannot use a file' stung me into gaining a mastery of that instrument that I have never forgotten. LPP was a firm believer in the wide open regulator and early cut-off method of driving locomotives. 'The regulator, Harvey, should be regarded merely as a stop valve. The flow of steam to the cylinders is better regulated with the reversing gear which should be used like the gearbox in a car – steam should be throttled at the regulator only to avoid excessive speed.'

He also believed in smart acceleration from stations. His inspectors were well drilled in these techniques, and no man was passed for driving unless he adopted these methods which were well suited to Great Eastern engines. Later on, with the arrival of Great Central locomotives which worked best on the first port of the regulator and one-and-a-half turns on the reversing screw, this precept had to be qualified if hot big-ends were to be avoided.

Another of Mr Parker's instruction was that when drifting with steam shut off the reversing gear of piston valve locomotives should be placed in mid-gear. Doubtless this instruction originated from the numerous cases of wrecked motion occurring to the long-valve travel N7 tanks, which, if put into full gear when coasting at speed, especially when running bunker-first, would almost certainly break off their valve spindle guide bushes, drag down their valve spindles and generally play havoc with their inside Walschaerts gear. If on his journeys to and from his home at Chigwell LPP heard the snifting valve clattering as the locomotive entered the station its driver was summoned to the inspector's office for an explanation. On one of his visits to me at Wood Street he observed 'The engine of my train was being worked in a most peculiar manner – when I should have heard the engine I couldn't and when I should not have done so I did! Ride with that man, Harvey, find out what he is doing wrong, and put him right!'

The holiday relief duty that I enjoyed most was at Southend even if it did mean being on duty for fourteen hours. The standard rate of pay for relief duties were 3s 6d (17½p) per day or 12s 6d (62½p) up to 24 hours. I generally managed to get in a swim at Thorpe Bay during the slack period in the afternoon unless rain threatened, then the crowds rolled up at the station much earlier than the booked times of their special trains – 2s 0d (10p) return from Liverpool Street, 1s 9d (9p) from Ilford! Difficulty arose in finding men to work these earlier trains until the first crew of the return specials reported for duty, after which men were stepped up on to earlier trains than those they were scheduled to work provided they had the necessary route knowledge. The Southend men were a good crowd and handled their Belpaire-boiler 1500s (all fitted with ACFI feed water heaters) well. No 8559 of this class was fitted experimentally with long-travel/long-lap valves, subsequently adopted as standard for the rebuilt Class B12/3s.

At other times I would be sent to Liverpool Street to relieve one of the regular running foremen on the afternoon shift. Failures were covered as far as possible by utilising a locomotive released from an adjacent platform when the train it had brought in departed. This gave time for Stratford to send a replacement from its 'cab rank' where an assortment of tank engines was kept ready to cover such contingencies. What one did not do was to move a locomotive from one side of Liverpool Street station to the other, for this could not be done without going as far as Bishopsgate and bringing to a halt every train entering or leaving Liverpool Street's eighteen platforms. At Bank Holidays, I would undertake similar duties on a smaller scale at Chingford or Temple Mills, preparing my own in and out working as at Liverpool Street.

CHAPTER 7

RUNNING SHED FOREMAN

Promotion was desperately slow in the 1930s but at the end of 1935 on the strength of LPP's recommendation I was appointed Grade II Running Foreman at Gorton, Manchester. I travelled there from Marylebone on Armistice Day 1935, the two minutes' silence, then most scrupulously honoured, being observed as my train stood in Leicester Central Station.

In striking contrast to the modernity of the Great Central London extension the atmosphere at Gorton was definitely that of its Victorian antecedent, the Manchester, Sheffield & Lincolnshire Railway, notably in its local trains of ancient six-wheel coaches hauled by Thomas Parker's radial tank engines fitted with Joy's valve gear.

My appointment was to supervise generally the working of the depot on the afternoon and night shifts, also to give decisions on mechanical matters (for which the running foremen being ex-footplate men were not qualified) in order to avoid locomotives being stopped unnecessarily for attention later by the day shift. This was the first time such duties had been combined in one job.

Apart from a few prestige passenger trains and the provision of power for the Cheshire Lines Committee, Gorton's principal duty was the working of heavy freight and mineral trains across the Pennines. The depot at Gorton was a difficult one to work. The yard layout, hemmed-in by neighbouring works and dwelling houses, was not only long and straggling (over 600yd between inlet and shed front) but it had an acute bottleneck where some twenty shed roads converged into two lines of metals at Bessemer Street bridge, over which all incoming and outgoing locomotives had to pass. Here the running foremen were located in a former signalbox always referred to as 'the Lighthouse' where they marshalled the shed in chalk on a long blackboard divided into numbered columns, one for each shed road. As each incoming locomotive passed they would shout to the berthing crew the number of the road on which they wished it to be placed. The berthing crews were assisted in their task by boards at each pair of points indicating the group of roads that these served. The chargehand cleaner in the oil stores was also notified by telephone, and it was his duty to chalk up on a duplicate board at the bottom of the shed the locomotive numbers and times of the train that they were booked to work.

Beyond the Lighthouse in the Manchester direction and parallel to the main line were two long wet ashpits and beyond these again a mechanical coaling plant with storage capacity of 200 tons, and last of all the locomotive inlet and outlet. It was here that the ashpit foreman was stationed to regulate the disposal and dispersal of incoming locomotives. On him depended the smooth working of the whole depot, especially at the changeover of shifts by the fire-droppers who were on piecework. These men having completed their quota for the day would do no more, possibly through fear of having their rates cut. Consequently a delay of up to two hours could occur before the oncoming shift had dealt with its first locomotive. Meanwhile locomotives waiting to be moved had lost their steam, and it only needed later arrivals to pile up and block the avoiding line for chaos to reign. On a subsequent visit to Gorton during World War II, I found the local lines blocked as far back as the next station at Guide Bridge by dead engines left by their crews when no more men were available to relieve them. On that memorable Sunday morning the line was cleared by raising steam in every fifth engine and using them to drag the others clear. With the depleted staff available, disposal took nearly two days. This fiasco brought home to me very forcibly the advantage of having ashpits arranged in parallel rather than series wherever possible.

I was also responsible for attending breakdowns occurring on my turn of duty, other than those blocking the main line. Those were dealt with by Ernest Maugham, the senior mechanical foreman, an outstanding personality at Gorton who was regarded by his men with affection and greatly respected for his ability as an engineer. Ernest had his own ideas as to what was needed to keep a locomotive in good repair and these differed considerably from the official schedule, to which he had to pay lip service. He knew for instance from long experience that if crossheads were re-metalled and piston glands overhauled, the incidence of blowing glands during the winter months would be greatly reduced. In his view a locomotive thoroughly repaired should run for six months with the minimum of intermediate attention. Neither had he any time for specialists – a man who could not turn his hand to a variety of jobs was of no use to him! His fitters were divided into groups each responsible for certain locomotives and he held the leading hands responsible for any shortcomings in their performance.

I owe a great deal to Ernest Maugham, who I regarded as an excellent example of the old school of Manchester engineer, both versatile and resourceful. For example, he had adapted his wheel lathe to turn journals long before the machine tool makers marketed such attachments, by the simple expedient of mounting a slide rest from an old lathe on a pedestal made from hydraulic piping and getting the speed he wanted by applying a driving belt directly to the tyres. It is of historical interest to record that the workshop machinery was driven by one-half of an engine from one of Sturrock's steam tenders of which the MS&L had several examples. He also showed me the places at the end of Nos 1 & 2 roads where slack tyres were once heated and expanded by gas jets for the insertion of strips of tin in the poverty-stricken days of the old Sheffield company! Ernest's hobby was photography, and frequently he would supplement his breakdown reports with excellent photographs of these incidents.

While at Gorton I had my first experience of disconnecting an engine and bringing it home on one cylinder. On 15 February 1936 Director class No 5433 *Walter Burgh Fair* (the one that I worked on at Neasden nine years earlier) failed in Woodhead tunnel by breaking its left big-end strap when working the 4.55pm down express from Marylebone. Fortunately for me it had been pulled out of the tunnel and placed in a siding at Dunford Bridge when I arrived on the scene with a fitter who disconnected the broken big-end strap while I secured the piston head, which was resting on the bogie. This done, I centred and secured the valve on the damaged side and with the help of a crowbar borrowed from a nearby platelayers' hut got the sound side into a suitable position for starting on our journey back to Gorton. I am unlikely to forget the thrill and satisfaction of hearing for the first time the sound of a locomotive with only one effective cylinder – the long interval between exhaust beats seemed quite uncanny!

In 1936 I contracted to do two tours of service as Chief Running Inspector on the Nigerian Railway returning home on 2 May 1940.

CHAPTER 8

WARTIME
TECHNICAL ASSISTANT

My return home from Nigeria on leave in May 1940 coincided with the end of the 'phoney war.' The evacuation from Dunkerque, the entry of Italy into the war on the side of the Axis, the fall of France on 17 June 1940 were grim news items indeed and brought the prospect of the long threatened invasion very near. In these circumstances I felt less than ever inclined to return to Nigeria now that I had completed my contract. Discreet enquiries as to the possibility of re-engagement by the LNER resulted in an interview at King's Cross with C. K. Bird, Regional General Manager, who offered me the temporary post of Technical Assistant at Colwick, subject to a satisfactory medical examination. On 8 July a letter confirmed his offer, which I accepted on the advice of my old chief Leslie Parker. Accordingly I tendered my resignation to the Colonial Office and on 8 August 1940 took up my new duties at Colwick, sharing an office with H. T. White, the Assistant District Locomotive Superintendent.

Colwick, the principal shed of the Great Northern in the Nottingham district, was situated about four miles to the east of that city and was the gathering point for the GNR lucrative coal traffic from the Nottinghamshire and Derbyshire pits. After the 1923 amalgamation it doubled in importance, for it then also became responsible for working the former Great Central heavy north–south coal traffic between Annesley and Woodford, with its associated depots, as well as the west–east traffic over the GNR.

One of the first jobs that I had was to see that every locomotive was equipped with a ring spanner to fit the injector delivery cap nuts, which in the event of invasion were to be removed and either hidden or destroyed, so rendering the locomotive useless to the enemy! Every driver was seen by Mr White, who read to him the instructions on how to immobilise his locomotive and obtained his signature as having understood the instructions. There was as usual the odd man out who would not sign – one gave as his reason that he had no quarrel with any German, as long as he was a good trade unionist, while a few thought that they should be armed with rifles! Essential parts to be removed from coaling plants and other vital equipment in the event of invasion were identified with yellow paint. Another task was the application of blister gas detector paint to cab spectacle glasses, which in the event of contamination developed red spots. Unfortunately these quickly became so covered with soot and grime as to be useless. Railway-sponsored ARP courses involving heavy manual work while wearing the civilian duty respirator and full protective clothing were also instituted. I joined the Gedling platoon of the 5th Nottinghamshire battalion of what had become the Home Guard and took my turn in the nightly patrol of Gedling woods.

I went out with the 36-ton Cowans Sheldon breakdown crane, with a long jib and relieving bogies, on several very interesting jobs. On one occasion at Annesley, after completing the job to which we had been summoned, we were asked by the yardmaster to re-rail an empty box van that had been projected over the buffer stops. We set up the crane with its long jib at right-angles, reaching across an intervening road to the van which was empty and weighed about 7½ tons, well within the crane's capacity at that radius when free on the rail with the rail clips in use. The van had just been lifted clear of the buffer stops when there was a loud report like a gunshot as the near side rail broke and the jib with its load dropped suddenly, causing the track on the far side to lift out of the ballast as the rail clips tightened and the crane started to capsize. Fortunately in Frank Hallam we had a first-rate cool-headed crane driver who promptly released the brake, allowed the load to drop and the crane to regain an even keel. It was then disclosed that the track on which we were standing had been freshly ballasted with ash ballast only the day before; a lesson in not taking the stability of ground for granted!

The maintenance in efficient condition of the tarpaulin anti-glare sheets on tender engines was a continual problem. Anti-glare sheets were to all intents and purposes the familiar storm sheet used when running tender-first in bad weather. These sheets were attached at one end to hooks on the cab roof and tied at the other to a rail spanning the tender front by short pieces of thin rope. If stretched taut, the relative movement between locomotive and tender would quickly tear the sheets, and if left slack they would sag and seriously restrict the headroom on the footplate. I rode one hot summer evening in the cab of a GN Class K2 so equipped, and am unlikely to forget its discomfort. Condensation from a blowing steam joint combined with a sagging sheet smothered in coal dust, plus the heat from the fire, turned the cab into a kind of infernal turkish bath. How we envied the Great Western enginemen their company's arrangement of long coil springs for keeping their sheets taut without risk of tearing. The extra initial cost of this refinement must have paid for itself many times over, by avoiding the continual renewal of anti-glare sheets, caused by the more primitive arrangement.

The summer of 1941 was spent mainly on relief duties at former Great Central sheds between Sheffield in the north to Woodford Halse in the south. With the exception of the first named these were all of the standard New Line pattern, differing only in the location of the offices and ancillary buildings; those at Staveley and Annesley were on the right, elsewhere on the left.

In complete contrast to the spacious New Line sheds the old Manchester, Sheffield & Lincolnshire Railway depot in Sheffield at Neepsend was cramped in the extreme. The line was carried through the city on arches and the small dead end shed at Neepsend stood on a shelf cut in the rocky hillside. So restricted was the ashpit accommodation that there was room for only one tender engine between the shed front and the small turntable and even this could not be used at night owing to the blackout regulations. In consequence, fires were dropped and smokeboxes emptied in the inspection pits inside the shed, making the proper preparation of locomotives not only difficult but sometimes impossible. The new shed at Darnall was then in course of construction and its progress towards completion gave much needed hope and encouragement to the hard-pressed staff at Neepsend who had been battling for so long under increasingly adverse conditions. Despite these handicaps, morale was high and the standard of mechanical maintenance excellent – piston glands and cylinder cocks, for example, were overhauled to a standard not usually seen outside a main works.

Bookings against 'glands and sands' were common in hilly districts due to the power that a locomotive had to exert in hauling heavy loads uphill, whereas bookings of indifferent steaming were few compared with those on the level lines of Lincolnshire or the fens of East Anglia where the demand for steam was constant and there were no downhill stretches on which to recover pressure.

Local conditions had their effect. Woodford men complained about the O4 class 2–8–0s working between Annesley and Woodford bumping between locomotives and tenders due to slackness in the drawgear. This was tightened regularly at Woodford, only to be slackened again on arrival at Annesley to enable the locomotives to negotiate the sharp curves in colliery sidings without becoming derailed!

Annesley, a halt on the Great Central main line a few miles to the north of Nottingham was important as a depot in that there was marshalled all the Great Central coal traffic to Woodford and the south and west. Annesley shed, hemmed in by Newstead colliery to the west and the main line separating it from Lord Byron's estate to the east, was unique in my experience in that few of the staff lived there; most lived in the suburbs of Nottingham, travelling to and from their work in the 'Dido', a Sentinel steam railmotor shuttle service between Annesley and Bulwell Common, operating 24 hours a day, seven days a week. The comings and goings of footplate staff in particular were dictated by the pattern of the Dido service. All too often it was found that a man with time to spare could not be utilised because his time of booking-off at Bulwell Common would incur either excessive hours on duty or interfere with the statutory rest period.

My chief recollection of the shed master's office at Annesley was its martial aspect; most prominent was an arms rack containing the railway Home Guard's M17 rifles, and suspended from the ceiling models of enemy aircraft to aid identification. Exploration of drawers in search of timetables and working instructions produced some unexpected finds in the shape of Army training manuals and clips of service rifle ammunition.

The southern destination of the block coal trains from Annesley was Woodford Halse, the junction for Banbury and the south and west of England. There could be no greater contrast than between these two depots, for whereas Annesley had no resident population and was sited next to a colliery tip, Woodford, a pleasant village built mainly of Cotswold stone in the Northamptonshire uplands, was essentially a railway village community which relied for its employment on the railway marshalling yard, locomotive depot and a well-equipped wagon repair shop.

Due possibly to its elevated situation, nearly 600ft above sea level, the precarious supply of water at Woodford was always a cause of some anxiety, despite the fact that the infant river Cherwell ran through the village from its source above the Catesby tunnel. The principal supply was pumped from two deep wells beneath the station tank house, supplemented by a large pond with its own pump house near the shed outlet, while about a mile to the north was yet another supply from a borehole at Preston Fields.

As at most country depots, the Woodford men took great pride in their work and were renowned for their quick turnround of locomotives, mainly Robinson 2-8-0s working the Annesley – Woodford coal trains and War Department traffic such as tanks, guns and munitions. Two sets of men, one disposing and the other preparing, regularly would have a locomotive back in service inside 45 minutes.

Many were lodging turns, the crews lodging in barracks near the shed. Due to wartime food rationing, difficulties arose in feeding men away from their home stations and for these a supply of tinned provisions was kept under lock and key in the shedmaster's office.

During one of these spells of relief duties at Woodford, the water troughs at Charwelton were cleaned out and it was interesting to compare the two designs of trough in use. That on the up line was of a plain rectangular section, relatively narrow and deep, whereas the trough on the down road was of the GWR pattern, broad and shallow with inward-turning lips at the top to reduce splashing. About this time an anti-splash device, consisting of a pair of inclined vanes or wings which cut the water in advance of the scoop snout into which it was guided, began to be fitted to the more modern LNER locomotives. This device was effective but until modified caused difficulty in raising the scoop due to the wings spreading and binding against the scoop protection shield.

When the Blitz started in September 1940 King's Cross did not escape unscathed for a bomb fell on the top shed, breaching the shed wall adjacent to the road known as the Continent, derailing a heavy 2-8-0 mineral engine yet leaving a stack of firebricks undisturbed – such are the odd effects of blast. This was followed on the 11 May 1941 by the dropping of two 1,000 lb bombs chained together on the terminus at King's Cross, bringing down four of the roof spans on the departure side and demolishing part of the office block; the gap in the Western façade exists to this day. The location of the Assistant Locomotive Superintendent's residence at the Top Shed has already been described. The effect of a bomb so close to it, coupled with the many disturbances of rest caused by being continuously on call, as well as the incessant alerts, brought about a breakdown in the health of its occupant, Bernard Adkinson, who removed to Hatfield and was on the sick list for over six weeks, during which period I deputised for him.

Many changes had taken place at the top shed during my ten years' absence. Robo's lift and the radial pits of the former round shed had gone, while adjacent to the stores now stood a wagon-hoist type mechanical coaling plant and a water softener. The greatest change of all, however, was in the staff. During the war all young men on attaining the age of eighteen were called up for military service and because railway service was a reserved occupation vacancies created by retirements were filled by men and women directed to it by the Ministry of Labour. Trade apprenticeship virtually ceased for the duration of the war, and with the consent of the trade unions suitable semi-skilled men were upgraded to skilled jobs and elderly men encouraged to work on beyond retiring age. After the war much publicity was given to filling vacancies created by the missing age group. As the war went on this shortage of skilled staff became progressively worse and to cover footplate vacancies a new grade of fireman, known as NLP (Non Line of Promotion) fireman was created to help reduce the excessive hours being worked by the diminishing number of regular firemen promoted to drivers. Normally two or three weeks' intensive training and instruction in essential operating rules was given to these men before putting them on pilot duties, but at Neasden the shortage of firemen was so acute that on at least one occasion in order to avoid the cancellation of a train, an NLP recruit with less than a week's tuition was sent out firing on the surburban service, thereby placing a heavy responsibility on the driver.

Men were also seconded from the armed forces for firing duties during three-monthly periods of rest, notably RAF bomber crews, who acquitted themselves nobly. We also had at Neasden soldiers from the Canadian Army Transportation Corps. At King's Cross, 40 women engine cleaners had replaced their male counterparts and were using as a mess room, and for changing rooms the Assistant Locomotive Superintendent's house which had been repaired. These women, (known to some as 'Harvey's

Lovelies') were a pretty tough crowd and for a fortnight staged a
sit-in strike after being suspended from duty for persistently
defying the management ruling that ceasing work 45 minutes
before their day was up was unreasonable and excessive. Their
presence round the shop heating stove was quickly betrayed by
the odour of violets then used as the olefactory agent in the centre
big-end heat detector and which they used as a perfume! This
scent was subsequently changed first to aniseed and then to garlic
on account of the persistence of the violet perfume, which would
hang round a locomotive for some days after the heat detector had
discharged!

I was destined to relieve at King's Cross on numerous occasions
during the next nine years. As railway wages fell behind those paid
outside, coupled with a general disinclination of new entrants to
work shifts, I found increasing difficulty in recruiting staff of the
right calibre, and ultimately of any kind. This trend,
characteristic of all the London depots at which I have relieved,
was not reversed until the early 1950s which saw the Indian
summer of steam at the Top Shed in the exemplary running of the
A4 Pacifics and the exploits of Bill Hoole on such trains as the
Elizabethan and Talisman with loads far in excess of those
handled before the war.

The problems of servicing and repairing steam locomotives at
night during the blackout were immense. Fires had to be allowed
to die down before being thrown out, while examination and
repairs had to be done outside in semi-darkness or wait until the
locomotives could be placed inside the shed. Later in the war
special light tunnels, resembling outsize Nissen huts, where
locomotives could be properly examined were installed at the
principal depots. Urban sheds were also badly affected in that
many of the staff relied on public transport to take them to and
from work, and during air raids their time of arrival on duty was
unpredictable. In such conditions it was not surprising that on 27
February 1941 three suburban passenger diagrams were cancelled
through shortage of power – ten N2s were out of service. On 20
March the back pit was roped off owing to the discovery there of
an unexploded anti-aircraft shell.

At the end of March I returned to the comparative peace of
Colwick where I received instructions from headquarters to carry
out an extensive investigation into the cost of repairing NE area
locomotives working into the Southern area, considered to be

The machine shop at Norwich motive power depot.

The wheel lathe at Norwich motive power depot. (*J. Bramwell*)

The old planing machine, *circa* 1856, at Norwich motive power depot. (*J. Bramwell*)

Norwich motive power depot during the enginemen's strike in 1955.
(*J. Bramwell*)
Class E4 2–4–0 No 62797 leaving Norwich Victoria on 8 September 1956 with a
Norfolk Railway Society special. (*Dr Ian C. Allen*)

excessive due to their allegedly poor condition. Allegations and counter-allegations of the 'pot calling the kettle black' description arose when there were differing standards of maintenance between depots, often due to circumstances beyond their control, such as a chronic shortage of staff or poor repair facilities. An exception to this very human trait was made in the case of the hard-pressed London depots during the war, when every assistance possible was given to them by the more fortunate country depots. My investigations took me to all the principal sheds regularly visited by NE area locomotives and a vast amount of evidence was accumulated and embodied in a lengthy report. Whether this told the NE authorities anything about the general conditions of the locomotives that they did not already know is doubtful.

One of the principal reasons for the deterioration in the standard of locomotive maintenance, apart from a shortage of skilled staff and interruptions due to air raids, was the enforced use of goods and mixed-traffic locomotives as common-user machines. Demands for power to work urgent Government specials could come literally at a moment's notice and then the first available locomotive, regardless of where it belonged, was turned out in order to avoid delay. In this way many became 'lost' for long periods, returning to their home depots only when in urgent need of washing-out, or overdue for boiler examination. So bad did the position become that a special weekly return of 'Engines away from their home depots for seven days or more' was instituted, catering for up to a month.

The effect of this indiscriminate use of motive power was that only the most urgent repairs to foreign locomotives to make them fit to work a train were carried out, all heavy repairs being reported to the home depots for attention. In consequence routine maintenance fell far into arrears, resulting in excessive wear and knock which if neglected induced fatigue fractures and ultimately breakage, particularly when accompanied by priming or the carry-over of water into the cylinders, as these sketches testify.

The wartime rationing of steel was another adverse contributing factor; components that ordinarily would have been renewed in Main Works on reaching their scrapping limit were often permitted to run for a further period, sometimes with disastrous results. For example, for many years I kept a section of a big-end strap from a GCR class A5 4–6–2T which had broken

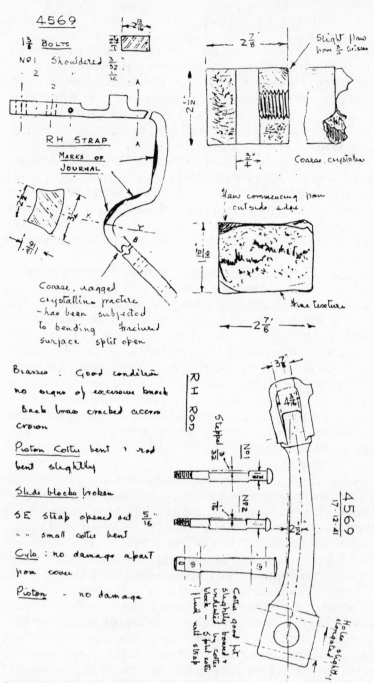

4569

1 3/8 BOLTS

N°1 Shouldered 3/32"

RH STRAP

MARKS OF JOURNAL

Coarse, ragged crystalline fracture — has been subjected to bending fractured surface split open

Slight flaw from 3/8 cristao

2 7/8

2 1/2

3/4

Coarse crystallue

Flaw commencing from outside edge.

fine texture

2 7/6

Brasses : Good condition no signs of excessive knock
Back brass cracked across crown

Piston cottu bent & rod bent slightly

Slide blocks broken

SE strap opened out 5/16"
" " small cotter bent

Cyl: no damage apart from cover

Piston - no damage

PROV IN

Stepped 3/32

No. 1

No. 2

2 1/2"

3 7/8

4 3/16

4569

17.12.41

Locmotive 4569, broken big end and strap

through the back bolt holes, due to these having been enlarged to 1⅞in from the original diameter of 1½in, thereby reducing the strength of the 3in wide strap to approximately three-quarters of its original value.

The death of Sir Nigel Gresley on 5 April 1941, dismayed and saddened us all. It was hard to realise that the era in which his creative genius had raised the prestige of British locomotive design and performance to a new high level was at an end. A future without HNG was inconceivable – to those of us who were proud to have participated even in a small way in the great events of his long period of office, the prospect was bleak indeed.

In the autumn of 1941 I was transferred to Gerrards Cross, the temporary wartime headquarters of the Southern Area of the LNER. 'Churston', a pleasantly situated detached villa near the railway bridge in Bull Lane, was where the Locomotive Running Superintendent G. A. Musgrave and his staff had their quarters.

In order to keep in touch with the realities of railway life, I made a practice of riding daily and often firing the locomotive of the 8.38am from Marylebone to Gerrards Cross. This train was worked by the men in Neasden No 2 link, whom I got to know quite well, and it was not long before I was invited to drive. One of my happiest memories of these times was their cheery greeting as I stepped aboard 'She's all yours!' This was invaluable experience in judging braking distances in all kinds of weather, also in picking up landmarks in fog. It is under these conditions, when a fear of over-running a stop signal is balanced by a desire not to lose time unnecessarily through being unduly cautious, that the true worth of a driver is really understood. The regular load for the A5 tanks was five compartment type bogie coaches; the technique for stopping correctly on the rising gradient at the short sleeper platform at Denham Golf Club halt was to keep the regulator open until entering the platform and then to apply the brake when about an engine's length short of its northern end.

One foggy evening when traffic to Marylebone had been disrupted by enemy action, I travelled to Paddington on the footplate of a GWR locomotive and was profoundly impressed by the confidence and assurance that the comforting ting of the ATC bell or the warning note of the horn gave to the crew – very different from the strain and anxiety experienced when trying to discern the position of a semaphore arm looming up through the mist.

The duties of a headquarters technical assistant on the LNER consisted primarily of investigating locomotive casualties and failures and where design appeared to be at fault, suggesting how it could be improved, also preparing drawings of alterations proposed. Great importance was attached by management to the casualty reporting system as a means of bringing to light troublesome features in design, bad workmanship or poor organisation.

The miles run per locomotive casualty was (and still is) regarded as a good indicator of the efficiency of any particular district or depot – 70,000 miles was considered a good figure. Responsibility for taking disciplinary action where staff were at fault remained with the districts. Only when it was necessary to ensure equality of treatment for the same offence, as in cases of signals passed at danger, did headquarters intervene. Casualties were divided into two categories, debitable and non-debitale. In the first category were all cases of delays exceeding five minutes to a passenger train or fifteen minutes to a goods train caused by a mechanical defect or breakdown – heated axleboxes, big-ends, or a fused lead plug were also ranked as failures even if no delay had been caused. Classed as non-debitable were delays caused by mismanagement, overloading, abnormal weather conditions, priming, shortage of water and slipping, provided no mechanical defect existed. The monthly analysis revealed how many casualties were due to faulty material, faulty design and faulty workmanship at works or at sheds.

Most important of all, as a means of improving the breed, it pinpointed those classes of locomotives and items of equipment that gave the most trouble, for example so many cases of J39 class 0–6–0 gudgeon pins coming out or so many heated middle big-ends on Pacifics. The J39 motion was identical with that of the modified GC Director class locomotives built for Scotland in having a four-bar motion and piston valves above the cylinders actuated by rocking shafts. I cannot recall any cases of gudgeon pins coming out on the inside-cylinder GC locomotives, but it was a frequent occurrence on a J39. The castle nut securing the gudgeon pin would loosen, shear its split pin and then work off, thus allowing the gudgeon pin to work out and foul the valve rocker, breaking its brackets in the process. I had practical experience of this on 28 July 1943 when the train in which I was travelling to Marylebone was terminated at Northolt Junction on

2501

A-3 (YORK) Inspected at
Leicester on 25/10/40
Failed at Rotherley on 24/10/40
in hands of running driver + Button
when working a sp[?] of gas cylinder
will heated middle [?] driven — slap
broken + never wearing
AB syphon top + crk intact but
driven into top of well by sliding
something

Blue as if tempered
— sound material

Bruh[?] has been [?] at 7/8
[?] heat

PIN TRIMMING
MISSING so
allowing oil
to escape

Cause
Absence of pin
trimming allowed oil
to run away +
lack of [?] in [?]
heat detector would
give no warning of
heating

Tender
Water Scoop — missing

LH W.S. bracket broken but
stay intact with nuts

Brake Cross Stay — broken
Nos 3 & 4 missing
out 6' Left & No2 L
and No4 on RH
broken — dented

Vac Reservoir
NoG Damage to [?]
appears to be independent
of big end failure +
disintegration of brasses.

First Conclusion: EMPTY + no
trace of [?]
Thermostat — Has operated
Big End Brasses — missing
Cyl. Beading — Appears intact
(slide unrended)
Cyl Cover — broken
Piston Head — marked as ⊙
Slide Bars (M) — Bent
Plate Stay (in front of Driving
box) — bent
dib[?]
lug broken off
RH Sand box
Angle Stay
Pistons — to examine

Locomotive 2501, broken centre big end strap

account of a locomotive failure in the section ahead. Standing on the curve about a quarter-mile away was a J39 and guessing the reason I went forward to investigate. As I suspected, No 3090's right-hand gudgeon pin had come out, wrecking the motion. Assistance had been summoned, but I sought to reduce the delay by getting on with the work of disconnection, borrowing the driver's slop (overall jacket) and using what tools I could find – a monkey wrench, a very blunt chisel and in the absence of a hand hammer, the coal pick. I had succeeded in removing with these unhandy tools the big-end cotter and all four nuts of the big-end bolts before assistance arrived. Consequently I was in a strong position to refute the charge made by control that undue delay had occurred in dealing with this failure. The first alteration in design was to reverse the position of the nut (which was made larger) from the outside to the inside slide block in order to make it more accessible but this only made matters worse, for now when the pin worked out it fouled the leading hornblock, bending and fetching down the slide bars. This trouble was finally exorcised by doing away with a nut fastening and making the hole in the slide blocks of lesser diameter than that in the small-end bush; the pin could no longer come out, but it did involve lifting the whole heavy assembly in one piece and sliding it into position between the slide bars from the rear.

An interesting example of an alteration in design to suit the changed conditions of wartime operation and maintenance, was that made to the heat detector unit fitted in the middle big-end crank pin of three-cylinder locomotives. This was fitted originally to locomotives working the non-stop high-speed trains between London and Edinburgh, in order that the driver should have advance warning of any dangerous rise in temperature of the middle big-end by the pungent odour released when the wax thermostat melted. The principal depots on the East Coast main line were provided with a supply of fluid and the means of recharging the fluid container in the event of heating. In wartime conditions the A4 class 4–6–2s found their way to many small depots, where the fitting staff were probably unaware that such a device existed, and even if they did they had neither the fluid nor means of recharging the fluid container. Several bad cases occurred of middle big-end straps collapsing through being brought to forging heat by the pounding caused on closing the regulator, following the disintegration and loss of the brasses due to excessive heating. This invariably happened when the regulator is closed and there was no longer steam to cushion the heavy reciprocating masses.

A good illustration is that of A3 class No 2501 *Colombo* that failed at Rothley on 24 October 1940 with a collapsed middle big-end, caused by the absence of the pin trimming that regulates the oil feed. The wax thermostat had operated but no warning of impending heating was given as the fluid container was found empty, nor was there the slightest trace of the smell of violets. In order to overcome the difficulty of recharging the fluid container, G. A. Musgrave suggested that it should be made easily removable, so that a freshly-charged unit could be drawn from the stores and inserted in the hollow crankpin. I was given the task of redesigning the unit, which hitherto had been expanded into the crankpin like a boiler tube, in order to ensure good conductivity, and that it did not loosen through centrifugal forces.

An interesting problem then arose; how best to overcome the difficulty caused by a slight variation in diameter of the bore of the hollow crankpins. This was solved eventually by the application of a split cone fastening, similar to that securing the gudgeon pins of the Nigerian Garratt locomotives. The Chief Mechanical Engineer gave his approval to this modification and issued Drawing No T566, a copy of my original, which became the standard design.

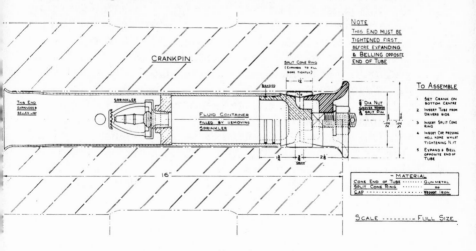

SUGGESTED AGGᵗ FOR REMOVABLE FLUID CONTAINER

When riding on the footplates of Pacifics, I was very concerned to note that many drivers were in the habit of tying up the application handle of the Metcalfe vacuum brake ejector in a loop of string in order to overcome its tendency to drop into the 'on' position. The urgent need to find a satisfactory alternative to this dangerous makeshift was obvious. What was not so clear was why the Metcalfe ejector, that had given long and trouble-free service on other classes of GN locomotives should suddenly develop this fault when applied to Pacifics. Investigation revealed that in the Pacific application, in order to clear the small ejector steam valve, the brake handle had been made 3in longer and therefore, six ounces heavier than those fitted to the Atlantics. This problem was solved by applying a counterweighted arm to the opposite end of the brake handle.

This solution was taken up by the manufacturers and can be seen to this day on the brake handle of No 4771 *Green Arrow* and other wide-firebox types, demonstrating yet again the truth of the age-old engineering axiom that there can be no action without a corresponding reaction. Yet another example of this elemental truth is the position of the slaking, or coal watering cock, on LNER locomotives, fitted originally to the injector on the fireman's side and therefore in constant use, but moved to the driver's side at the suggestion of C. M. Stedman, Locomotive Running Superintendent of the NE area, as a means of ensuring that this injector, often found unworkable through lack of use when required was used regularly. The drivers objected that the firemen got in their way when operating the slaking cock in its new position. The solution was to return the cock to its original position on the fireman's side but to connect it by a pipe to the driver's injector.

One of the earliest and most interesting jobs that I had at Gerrards Cross was to investigate the cause of the indifferent steaming of the ex-Metropolitan Railway 0–6–4 tanks of the Lord Aberconway class working the London Passenger Transport Board service between Rickmansworth and Aylesbury. Prior to the extension of its electrified lines to Rickmansworth, the Metropolitan's small fleet of steam locomotives had been maintained in tip-top condition at its Neasden depot. These were supplied with the best hand-picked Welsh steam coal. From 1937 onwards the LNER as partners in the joint line became responsible for working the Metropolitan's steam-hauled trains north of Harrow, locomotives and men being transferred to the Great Central shed. On paper this arrangement may have shown an economy but in practice it could not have done so, for the Metropolitan still had to maintain its steam shed for a handful of 0–6–2Ts, a 4–4–0T, and its Peckett 0–6–0T. At the GC shed conditions were similar to those prevailing at joint depots on the Cheshire Lines, for there were now two separate and distinct sets of enginemen, neither of whom was permitted to undertake the others' duties. The ashpits might be congested with Great Central locomotives awaiting disposal due to shortage of relief staff, yet at the same time there might be Metropolitan men sitting in their mess room waiting orders, who could not be utilised, and vice versa. The only real pooling of resources was in boiler-washing and locomotive repairs. An immediate effect of this transfer of maintenance to the GC shed was a decline in the condition of the Metropolitan locomotives as the LNER employed fewer fitters to maintain a given number than did the Metropolitan company. Delays in getting long-standing defects rectified by a hard-pressed staff, was undoubtedly responsible for a feeling of discontent among many of the Metropolitan men, yet very few elected to return to the other side as electric motormen, such was the spell of steam!

A general decline in the standard of maintenance and in the quality of coal resulted in more and more bookings of indifferent steaming of classes of locomotive that hitherto had given no trouble, two of these being the H2 class 4–4–4T and M2 class 0–6–4 tank engines of the former Metropolitan Railway. I was concerned with No 6154 *Lord Aberconway*, one of the 0–6–4 tanks. The first step was to make sure that these were no air leaks or blowing steam joints to destroy the draught in the smokebox, also to see that the air spaces between the fireboxes were not blocked, nor the tubes, and that steam was not being wasted by leaking past valves and pistons. These several points having been verified and the relevant dimensions in the smokebox checked against the drawing, the next step was to establish what increase in draught was required to burn more coal of a lower calorific value, in order to produce the same amount of heat as from a lesser quantity of high quality steam coal.

Prior to the systematic and scientific testing of locomotives on the test plants at Swindon and Rugby, draughting was still very much a question of trial and error despite the abundance of

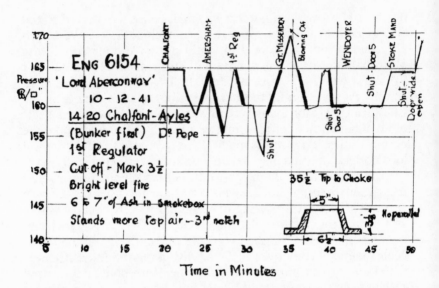

Time in Minutes

empirical formulae, some extremely complex, available to designers. At the other end of the scale came such gems of rule of thumb as raising a locomotive at its front end in order to allow the smoke to roll out of the tubes more easily, or inclining the blastpipe towards the smokebox door – not less than ⅛in for a goods engine or ³⁄₁₆in for fast engines!

A careful study of drawing I715 showing the smokebox proportions of 153 different classes and sub-classes of former GC, GE and GN locomotives, in the hope that I should find some common factor among those classes known to steam freely, was of no help – their dimensions were as diverse as the appearance of the locomotives themselves. In order to solve the problem, I fell back on the time-honoured method of trial and error. As originally designed, the M2s had a 5¼in blast orifice, quite large for a locomotive with two 20in cylinders. This was progressively reduced in diameter by the insertion of a ring or bush: a diameter of 5in was found to give the best results. On one occasion when approaching Amersham in the up direction this bush blew out of the blastpipe, leaving an orifice no less than 6½in in diameter with which to face another round trip to Aylesbury. Driver Pope however accepted this challenge to his skill quite philosophically, merely observing that provided he had a good fire and the injector was used sparingly, he thought that he could get through without

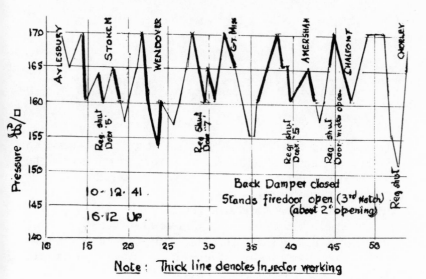

Note : Thick line denotes Injector working

loss of time. Leaving Rickmansworth, pressure fell rapidly from
130 lb/sq in to 120 lb/sq in and two minutes were lost in climbing
to Amersham, pressure having dropped to 110 lb/sq in at the
summit of the six-mile gradient. However, by using only the first
valve of the regulator, an early cut-off and sparing use of the
injector, a right-time arrival at Aylesbury was achieved. On the
return journey Driver Pope, to whom the greatest credit is due for
his skilful handling of the engine, did even better by arriving at
Rickmansworth one minute ahead of time!

Another remarkable case that was equally difficult to reconcile
with accepted theory occurred on 30 June 1960 when Britannia
class No 70041 came off its train at Ipswich with an aperture of no
less than 160 sq in in the top of its smokebox, caused by the
collapse under atmospheric pressure of the thin sheet steel casing
covering the superheater header, which had rusted away. This
defect, which in theory should have destroyed the draught
completely, caused a loss of time of only nine minutes due to the
locomotive's inability to maintain more than 160 lb/sq in pressure
in the boiler.

CHAPTER 9

THE USA LOCOMOTIVES

Early in 1943 the first US Transportation Corps 2–8–0s began to arrive in this country at about the same time as the first of the British-built Austerity 2–8–0s came into service. It was fascinating to compare the two designs, so dissimilar in every respect except for their wheel arrangement.

The American locomotives had wide-firebox boilers mounted above the trailing coupled wheels, something previously not seen in this country. They had bar frames made from 4½in slabs of steel, very strong to resist lateral forces, but weaker in a vertical direction than the conventional British plate frame. Another obvious difference was the small diameter of the smokebox door used in conjunction with a self-cleaning smokebox, which dispensed with the need to shovel out ashes by hand. It also had the advantage that being small it could be made of cast-iron and therefore was less liable to warp under heat than a large pressed-steel door.

I found the design particularly interesting because although in detail it reflected modern American practice, a locomotive so small that it could be hand fired had not been built for domestic use in the USA for many years. Apart from side buffers and screw couplings the only concession to British practice (at our request) was the use of oil as a lubricant instead of hard grease for the American pattern axlebox with its all-bronze bearing. In temperate climates the higher running temperature of an all-bronze bearing lubricated with hard grease can be a positive disadvantage by misleading drivers accustomed only to axleboxes lined with anti-friction metal, into thinking that every axlebox on their locomotives was hot! This happened on more than one occasion and I recall being sent post-haste to examine the axleboxes of 14 American 2–8–0s, all said to be hot. Five that were still warm I released immediately, the remainder on condition that on withdrawing the cellars or keeps the journal and axle pads were found to be in good order.

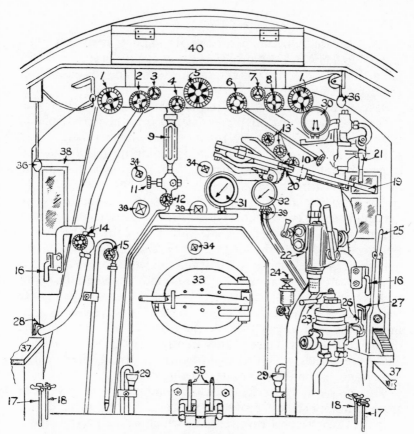

US 2–8–0 cab layout

1. Injector main stop valves.
2. Blower main stop valve.
3. Steam sand stop valve.
4. Steam brake stop valve.
5. Main stop valve for manifold.
6. Vacuum ejector steam stop valve.
7. Mechanical lubricator warming valve.
8. Air pump stop valve.
9. Water gauge.
10. Water gauge top stop valve.
11. Water gauge bottom stop valve.
12. Water gauge drain valve.
13. Boiler water level test valves.
14. Blower valve.
15. Coal slacker valve.
16. Injector steam valve handles.
17. Injector water control.
18. Injector overflow control.
19. Regulator handle.
20. Regulator handle locking pin.

21. Graduable steam brake valve.
22. Vacuum ejector.
23. Westinghouse brake valve.
24. Steam brake cylinder lubricator.
25. Reversing lever.
26. Steam sand valve.
27. Cylinder cock lever.
28. Blowdown cock lever.
29. Injector overflow indicator.
30. Duplex vacuum gauge.
31. Boiler-pressure gauge.
32. Westinghouse pressure gauge.
33. Firehole door.
34. Wash-out plugs.
35. Rocker grate levers.
36. Whistle controls.
37. Enginemen's seats.
38. Side door to footplate.
39. Water tube inspection plugs.
40. Locker for flags and detonators.

Hard grease lubrication on the Franklin system had been applied to GNR 2–6–0 No 1673 in the 1920s and was abandoned because this locomotive was continually being stopped on account of axlebox heating.

Several excellent features in the design of the American locomotives were soon adopted as standard for new construction in this country, notably the rocking grate, hopper ashpan and self-cleaning smokebox, all aids to speeding up the disposal of locomotives. It is chastening to reflect that Baldwin was supplying locomotives with rocking grates to China in 1898.

The rocking grate had important advantages over the drop grate – it could be shaken en route in order to clear ash and cinders from the fire and it enabled the whole contents of the firebox to be dumped quickly into the hopper ashpan and thence through the bottom discharge doors into the ashpit below. Unfortunately this facility was open to abuse by unscrupulous firemen anxious to make a smart getaway, dumping the fire into the ashpan while waiting at a terminal for the locomotive to be released. This malpractice warped and distorted the ashpan to an extent that the discharge doors no longer fitted tightly, thus allowing red hot cinders to escape, which if caught by the revolving wheel spokes were projected onto the lineside, starting fires.

The self-cleaning smokebox when combined with wire mesh spark-arresting screens proved to be less of an anti-social device than the Great Central ash ejectors to which we were accustomed.

Keeping the firebox circulating or arch tubes free from scale internally created special problems for Woodford where the 25 American locomotives allocated to the GC section were based. Half-moon shape rakes for scraping clean the interior surfaces of the circulating tubes were made, but owing to bends in the tubes these were only partially effective and it was not until the following year that a Sellars thread washout plug tap and a specially designed pneumatic tool for descaling the arch tubes arrived from America. In the meantime an increasing number of arch tubes started to blister and bulge, clear indication that overheating was taking place – so serious did this become that four or five locomotives a week were being taken into the main works for the renewal of defective arch tubes.

I reported to G. A. Musgrave on 22 January:

Bulged arch tubes

Four of the worst cases Engine Nos US 1840, 1847, 1848 and 1849 have already gone into the shops but there still remains in service twelve engines having such arch tubes bulged and blistered in varying degrees and considerable anxiety is felt regarding the safety of these engines.

I personally examined the arch tubes of Engine No US 1832 now stopped for piston repairs (core plug worked out) and found that the RH tube was bulged along its underside throughout its entire length and a blister about 2½in in diameter and protruding ⅛in had formed at a point immediately below the firebox end of the brick arch.

Judging from the appearance of the blister it was evident that the tube had been red hot at this point and had given under the pressure of steam. The middle and left hand tubes were bulged to a lesser extent.

Having regard to the condition of the RH tube and the serious consequences which may result from any further weakening thereof, I decided that it was inadvisable to allow this engine to continue in service and relying on your concurrence I instructed Mr Howe to stop this engine for shops forthwith at the same time advising him to deal in the same manner with the remaining engines should these exhibit bulges of similar magnitude to that observed on Engine 1832.

SkatOskalO descaling machine

A trial of this appliance was made on US Engine No 1731 the tubes of which are very slightly bulged and it was found necessary to use all three sizes (Nos 16, 17 and 18) of descaling heads provided to remove completely the coating of hard scale (approximately ⅛in thick) the whole operation taking roughly 1½ hours.

It is anticipated that this time will be reduced at future cleanings, as once the initial process of descaling has been effected, it should be unnecessary to use other than the largest size head (No 18) to keep the tubes clean.

A wire burnishing brush attachment is on order and when this is received it is proposed to burnish the interior of the tubes with black lead which should still further lessen the tendency for scale to adhere to the internal surface.

I am confident that once the defective tubes now in service have been renewed, the regular use of the SkatOskalO appliance for descaling will remove all further cause for anxiety by maintaining the tubes perfectly clean internally.

Welded Boiler Tubes

Owing to the hard water obtaining at Woodford, it is the practice at that depot to sift the boilers at six-monthly intervals by withdrawing a certain percentage of the tubes for the removal of scale. This process cannot be readily applied to the American engines due to the fact that the tubes are welded to the tube plate, therefore, I feel that consideration should be given to reallocating these engines to a better water district for this reason.

Nathan double seated type water gauge drain and test cocks

It was brought to my notice that due to the hard water in use and the peculiar construction of these cocks, it was necessary to remove these for cleaning with hydrocholoric acid at fortnightly intervals on account of the small (⅛in) cross-ports and grooves in the spindle becoming choked with scale. This is a serious defect and may lead to a false indication of water and I consider that the regulations laid down for the examination of the water gauges of the US engines should be amended in the light of this experience.'

A novelty was the extensive use of small diameter steel gas piping and screwed elbows for such items as lubricator, brake and water engine drain pipes where we would use copper; the lubricator pipes leading to the coupled axleboxes were carried under the boiler in a V-shaped trough of angle-iron in which rain and condensate was apt to collect, with the inevitable result that the pipes soon rusted through and had to be renewed in copper.

Another departure from British practice was the complete absence of syphon corks in the connecting and coupling rod oil wells – instead each was provided with two brass hexagon head filling plugs.

A grave fault from our point of view was the attachment of the reversing lever fulcrum to the firebox wrapper plate instead of to the frame as in British practice; kicking of the reversing lever in service caused the studs securing it to loosen.

The American locomotives did excellent work in this country before going overseas, the only real trouble experienced with them being caused by features in design that were ill-suited to British operating methods. For example, the double-bogie tenders had chilled cast-iron wheels in accordance with standard American practice. This was perfectly satisfactory in the USA where all trains were air-braked throughout, but not so in Great Britain where the tender hand-brake was used to assist the guard in holding back heavy loose-coupled freight trains when descending long falling gradients. Prolonged application of the tender hand-brake caused overheating of the wheel treads which developed scabs or flaking of the hardened surface. Sometimes whole segments of the flange would break off, as in the case of USA No 7076, stopped at Neasden on 22 November 1944 with 2ft of flange broken off one of the chilled-iron tender wheels.

Three cases of collapsed fireboxes due to low water occurred

Class B1 4–6–0 No 1042 leaving Norwich with the East Anglian express. (*Eastern Daily Press*)

Class B1 4–6–0 No 61043 in early BR lined black livery, at Norwich. (*British Rail*)

Class J15 0–6–0 No 65469 on a special train at Reepham, 17 April 1961.

'Like a jeweller's shop' – the boiler front of Class J15 No 5447, photographed at Laxfield, Mid Suffolk Railway. (*Dr Ian C. Allen*)

while the American locomotives were working in this country, the first at Honeybourne on the GWR, the second at Thurston near Bury St Edmunds with No 2363 in January 1944 and the third on 30 August 1944 while No 1707 was passing through Sudbury Hill tunnel, resulting in the death of the crew.

The cause of these dreadful disasters was a false indication of water in the gauge glass due to a partially-closed steam valve which was of the screw-down or wheel pattern. Plug cocks were invariably used for this purpose in the UK. With these the position of the cock handle showed at a glance whether it was open, closed or partially closed. Not so with the screw-down valve which had to be turned to find out whether it was open or closed, and even this method could be misleading if the valve happened to have a left-hand thread, as did some injector steam valves on Southern Railway locomotives.

As a result of these disasters the two ex GC and GE instruction coaches that continually toured the LNER system were promptly equipped with a small pressure vessel to which was attached a standard gauge column, in order to demonstrate to enginemen how a false water indication could occur and how it could be detected. The collapse of these all-welded steel fireboxes, tragic as they were, demonstrated beyond doubt the reliability of this mode of construction. In not one instance had rupture occurred at a weld, even where the plate had been folded back on itself after tearing through the solid metal where it had been weakened by a line of stay bolt holes.

The view through the firehole of No 1707 was awe-inspiring. Looking around and upwards the eye was met with a forest of roof and side stay bolts from which the red-hot crown sheet had been wrenched when it could be longer sustain the pressure. The ferocity of the ensuing explosion had then torn it apart at all four corners, forcing it downwards into a bowl shape at grate level; in appearance it resembled the inside of a gigantic colander. Strangely enough the screw threads in the stay holes had not been stripped, as might have been expected, due perhaps to the plastic condition of the red-hot plate. Another interesting fact that emerged as the plate became polished by the footwear of those making an examination of the firebox, was the appearance of ripples or undulations on its surface, clearly showing that tearing had been momentarily arrested each time a row of stays was encountered.

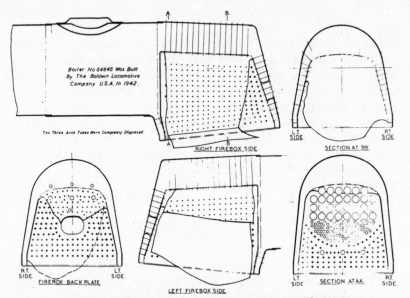

Boiler No 64646 Was Built By The Baldwin Locomotive Company U.S.A. In 1942.

The Three Arch Tubes Were Completely Displaced.

RIGHT FIREBOX SIDE

SECTION AT 'BB'.
L.T. SIDE   R.T. SIDE

FIREBOX BACK PLATE
R.T. SIDE   L.T. SIDE

LEFT FIREBOX SIDE.

SECTION AT AA.
L.T. SIDE   R.T. SIDE

AMERICAN 2-8-0 LOCOMOTIVE No. 1707 ALLOCATED TO WOODFORD LOCO: G.C.
Boiler Mishap In Sudbury Hill Tunnel G.C. Sect: On August 30th 1944 At 3-45 Approx:
Whilst Working The 2-45 Am Goods Neasden To Woodford.

Locomotive Running Supt.
Southern Area, Western Section.
L.N.E.R. GERRARDS CROSS.

The explosion occurred in the middle of Sudbury Hill tunnel where debris in the shape of ashpan plates, firebars, an arch tube and the smokebox door were found. Due to the momentum stored in the heavy locomotive and its unbraked load of 19 wagons, it continued on its way for a further 360yd before it was finally brought to rest by the braking action of the ashpan which had been forced downwards onto the trailing coupled wheels by the violence of the explosion. In order to clear the line the trailing side rods were removed and the locomotive drawn back through the tunnel with its trailing wheels locked and skidding.

In all three incidents the trains continued to travel onwards for considerable distances due to their own momentum despite the mechanical resistance of the disabled locomotives.

In contrast, there is little to record concerning the Ministry of Supply Austerity locomotives allocated to the New England depot at Peterborough, beyond a scare report that over 70 firebox stays were thought to be broken in one of the new 2-10-0s. The examiner had been misled by the dull sound of the Flanery flexible stays fitted in the wide fireboxes of these later Austerities. The only real trouble was a tendency of the fabricated rubbing blocks between locomotive and tender to collapse under the impact of heavy loose-coupled coal trains when the speed of these on falling gradients was checked by an application of the steam brake on the locomotive.

Ninety-one veterans from World War I, the ubiquitous Railway Operating Division (ROD) 2–8–0s of Robinson's design were also overhauled at Gorton and shipped to Persia as part of our strategy in the Middle East; it was said that all but one arrived safely.

The technical assistants also filled temporary vacancies at the depots, created by sickness or holidays. I spent much time at Neasden deputising for Matthew Robinson during his long periods of illness that led to his early retirement. Any interruption to the smooth running of the LPTB steam-hauled service between Rickmansworth and Aylesbury (for which the LNER had provided power since 1937), received the personal attention of its chairman, Lord Ashfield, while the GWR authorities were not slow in voicing their complaints if one of their Birmingham expresses was delayed. The all-too-frequent appearance of the Crab coal tank engines and Lord Faringdon class four-cylinder locomotives running tender-first on suburban passenger trains clearly indicated that all was not well at Neasden.

The root cause of absenteeism were the long periods worked without a break. As the war dragged on into its fourth year and more and more men retired, those that were left had to work longer hours due to the shortage of relief staff, while regular Sunday duty became the norm. The position was further aggravated by the almost total lack of living accommodation at Neasden for men from up country willing to transfer to fill firing vacancies. Many of the NLP firemen lived in South London and these when on early turn would travel overnight and sleep in an air raid shelter until it was time to report for duty. This difficulty was later overcome at the larger London depots by the provision of hostels.

As the end of the hostilities in Europe came into sight, thoughts began to concentrate on post-war planning and the opportunity this offered of carrying out schemes to modernise and enlarge many of the older depots, postponed by the war. Competition developed between the areas as to which could produce the best ideal shed. York devised a remarkable herringbone layout of a series of short engine spurs, each connected to a central through road by a set of points, in order to avoid the use of turntables in the round sheds favoured in the NE area. George N. Balfour produced an excellent design of through shed that avoided conflicting movements and where all operations were progressive. Unfortunately few of these post-war schemes materialised on account of either lack of room or money but they did much to raise our morale, for we felt that now the war was really over we could continue from where we had left off in 1939.

My contribution was in the field of locomotive design. I was chosen to represent the four locomotive running superintendents in investigating jointly with Bert Spencer, formerly Sir Nigel Gresley's personal draughtsman, weaknesses in design revealed by wartime conditions on certain selected classes of locomotives, and to suggest remedies.

A start was made with those common to all areas, the Pacific and V2 classes. All the principal depots on the East Coast main line between King's Cross and Edinburgh (Haymarket) were visited in turn and the views and suggestions of the maintenance staff canvassed. All complained of the deterioration in performance of the middle big-end and its tendency to run hot when subjected to additional loading caused by wear in the pins of the 2–1 gear due to ingress into their bearings of smokebox ash. The 2–1 gear was a simple and ingenious arrangement of two levers connecting the right- and left-hand valve gears in such a way that their combined motion gave a correct steam distribution to the middle valve, thus dispensing with the need for a separate inside valve gear. All advantages have corresponding disadvantages – any lost motion caused by wear in either of the outside gears was also imparted to the middle valve thereby increasing its port opening to steam and consequently the loading on the middle big-end. Over-running of the middle valve occurred at high speed due to whip in the two primary valve motions when these were subjected to heavy inertia forces. In peacetime with good maintenance and regular and thorough greasing, wear was easily contained within acceptable limits. The principal causes of excessive wear under war conditions were the ingress of fine smokebox ash into the bearings and over-long intervals between greasing. We recommended as a temporary expedient until pre-war standards of maintenance could be assured that an oil lubricated plain bearing of the largest possible diameter (which could be given attention by the driver) be substituted for the existing grease-lubricated main fulcrum roller bearing, also that special attention be given to making the footplating and inspection door above the 2–1 gear ash proof.

Twenty-one items in all were listed for attention ranging in importance from those just described, down to the allegedly poor war-time quality of the india rubber neck ring bushes used in vacuum brake cylinders, the short life of which we found was not caused by inferior material but to locomotives awaiting disposal standing over heaps of live fire carelessly dropped in the four foot.

Regarding the middle big-end about which so much has been written in recent years, the evidence produced at the depots we visited confirmed my opinion that the semicircular strap was weak and was flexing under load, thereby distorting the brasses and causing these to nip the journal and so cause heating. Proof that flexing occurred was afforded by the fact that when a centre big-end was taken down for examination the jaws of the two brasses were invariably bright and polished where one had fretted against the other – likewise the surfaces of the bronze shims or gluts used for adjustment. More convincing proof was the fact that whenever a brass was found broken in two, as happened occasionally, it was always the back brass that broke, never the front brass, although the front was weakened by a ¾in keyway preventing the circular brasses from rotating. The polished appearance of the fractured surfaces caused by fretting was convincing proof that the strap flexed. The design of the middle connecting rod and strap closely resembled on a larger scale that in a high class automobile engine and was a magnificent piece of forging and machining. Possibly its designer had such a prototype in mind but overlooked the fact that whereas an internal combustion engine was single-acting and the strap therefore carried little or no load, in a double-acting steam engine this was not so, for the loading was the same on both brasses, for which the strap as designed was ill-suited, being at its weakest at the point where it needed to be the strongest.

I had been much impressed by the excellent design of rod ends that I had seen on German locomotives. These were of T-section with a deep crescent-shaped rib or web at the back in order to resist deflection. This was the design that we recommended and which was ultimately adopted as the standard – not quite as we wanted, as the rib was made concentric instead of crescent-shaped, but still a good deal stiffer than the original design.

This improved pattern may be seen on nearly all the Gresley three-cylinder locomotives that have been preserved. Prior to this, several alternative designs of big-ends for three-cylinder

LNER

AMENDED DESIGN OF CENTRE BIG END STRAP

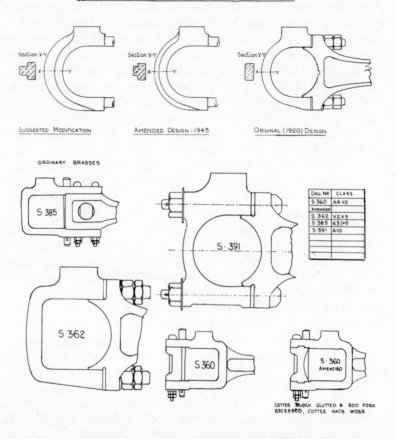

Section X-Y

SUGGESTED MODIFICATION

Section X-Y

AMENDED DESIGN : 1945

Section X-Y

ORIGINAL (1920) DESIGN

ORDINARY BRASSES

S 385

S·391

S 362

S 360

S·360 AMENDED

DRG Nº	CLASS
S 360	A4 V2
AMENDED	
S 362	V2 K3
S 385	K3 (M)
S·391	A10

COTTER BLOCK GLUTIED & ROD FORK
RECESSED, COTTER MADE WIDER

locomotives had been produced under Edward Thompson's direction but those seemed to be singularly unattractive in design, being heavy and clumsy. An interesting aspect of our enquiries was the diversity of opinions expressed on minor points of design, troubles experienced at one depot with certain fittings being almost unknown at another.

An increase in the number of heated coupled axleboxes on Pacifics and V2s also came under scrutiny. These 50 pattern axleboxes had a large bearing area and before the war seldom gave trouble with heating. It was suggested that lowering the rape content in the oil from 25% to 15% was responsible, but as this lower rape content oil was proving satisfactory under axlebox loading conditions much more severe than on the Pacifics or V2 classes there had to be some other cause. This was traced eventually to a change in Works procedure, in that the time-honoured (and time-consuming) practice of bedding axleboxes onto their journals by hand had been abandoned as a wartime economy measure. Instead, axleboxes were now bored out 0.014in larger than the journal and put on without fitting. This method resulted in the bearing having little more than line contact with the journal, causing the early development of knock and a liability to heat. A reversion to pre-war practice was therefore our recommendation.

A feature that formerly characterised the Gresley three-cylinder locomotives, the musical clang produced by the resonant lightweight alloy steel coupling and connecting rods which rang like a bell when struck with a hammer, disappeared in later years when these were replaced by rods made from ordinary carbon steel. The adoption of heat-treated nickel-chrome steel with a tensile strength of 60 tons for the motion of Gresley locomotives instead of ordinary 32.37 tons carbon steel succeeded in reducing by more than one-third the weight of the revolving and reciprocating masses, with a consequent reduction in rail hammerblow. This innovation stood the LNER in good stead in later years, for no alteration in wheel balance was necessary when alloy steel became unobtainable and heavier rods made from carbon steel had to be substituted, because this increase in weight was offset by a corresponding reduction in the reciprocating balance from 65% to 40%. The fact that O.V.S. Bulleid had eliminated reciprocating balance entirely in his own three-cylinder Pacifics, no doubt influenced Doncaster in making this change from hitherto accepted practice. These are the rods seen today on those Gresley locomotives that have survived, and although much lighter and more elegant than those fitted to BR standard locomotives of comparable power, they do seem to me heavy in appearance when I recall the beautifully light originals with webs only ⅜in thick.

CHAPTER 10

MECHANICAL FOREMAN

On 10 July 1945 I was interviewed at Liverpool Street Headquarters Offices by a committee consisting of the Assistant Divisional General Managers of the NE, Southern and Scottish areas and Mr Blair representing the Chief Mechanical Engineer's department. The chairman prefaced his remarks by stating that the interview was not in connection with any specific vacancy but was for the purpose of forming a cadre of technical officers on which they could draw as and when vacancies arose; also to gain personal knowledge of the applicant. At this interview I explained that as I was not eligible for vacancies in the line of promotion under the terms of my re-engagement, which was temporary, I was anxious to have that status revised now that the war in Europe was at an end.

Two months later I was asked by my old chief Leslie Parker if I would like to return to the Great Eastern section as Mechanical Foreman Special Class at Cambridge. 'Not much of job, Harvey, but it will lead to something better!' – which indeed it did, for within twelve months I was appointed Locomotive Shed Master at Norwich, a post that I held until my retirement in 1970.

The year that I spent at Cambridge was excellent training in learning how best to use the varied skills of a depleted labour force in overcoming arrears of maintenance of a fleet of more than 80 locomotives – twenty-three of those were B17 three-cylinder 4–6–0s with 2 to 1 gear behind the cylinders.

This period was particularly interesting as it saw the recruitment of men returning from the armed forces to fill the vacancies created by the 'missing age group'. The range and extent of the skills among these applicants for fitting vacancies varied enormously. Some were apprentice or service trained fitters while others had received but a few months' vocational training before returning to civilian life. When doubt existed as to the skill or competence of the latter they were given a simple trade test such as filing a hexagon on an oil cup syphon top to fit a 1⅛in ring spanner.

Some of my colleagues complained that these post-war appointees were of little immediate help owing to their ignorance of locomotive work, and in consequence they were relegated to stripping smokeboxes and other rough jobs. My own view was that provided a man was a competent tradesman he should be able to adapt himself after suitable instruction to a different branch of mechanical engineering from that in which he had been trained. I therefore gave each man as long a period as I could afford, generally from three to six weeks, working with an experienced railway fitter on valve and piston examinations, big-ends, and general running repairs including injectors and brakes. To those who were sufficiently interested to want to learn more about the locomotive I gladly gave personal instruction and explanations. This method of training paid off handsomely for I soon had men who could be safely entrusted to work on their own instead of acting as highly-paid assistants to other fitters, or doing lower grade work.

My chief concern was the run-down condition of the B17s employed on the London service to King's Cross and Liverpool Street together with the constant complaints from drivers about their rough state. Like the K3s, the B17s became increasingly uncomfortable to ride as lateral play developed in the trailing coupled axleboxes – the remedy was to drop the trailing wheels, metal-up the axleboxes for side play, rebore and reface. In most cases this sufficed to restore the locomotive to a good riding condition but there were instances when the axleboxes on the leading and middle pairs of coupled wheels also needed attention. While this work was going on, the opportunity was taken to carry out the standard examinations such as renewal of valve and piston rings, connecting and coupling rod bushes, overhaul of injectors, brakes and lubrication system, besides non-scheduled work like remetalling crossheads, renewal of piston packing, tightening of drawbars, firmly securing hornstays and the adjustment of wedges. The result of all this effort, which amounted to an intermediate works repair and which took about three weeks, was a good riding locomotive that I could rely on to run a further 40,000 miles without trouble or until called into shops.

The price that had to be paid for all this extra work was a temporary increase in the already high 'stop list' to 15% (the target figure for locomotives under repair and examination was 5%). This caused considerable apprehension and anxiety to my local chief who was under pressure from headquarters to bring this figure down to a more reasonable level, and from the running foremen who had difficulty in finding enough power to run the trains.

Often I helped Fred Carpenter, the Works Inspector, by rectifying defects on newly-repaired locomotives, which if returned to Works would have affected output and bonuses, while if he could manage it, he would help me by getting a high mileage locomotive that was uneconomical for me to repair into Works at less than its official scheduled mileage. I likewise resisted pressure from above to curtail the amount of work going into the overhaul of the B17s and in this I was supported by T. C. B. Miller, then Assistant District Locomotive Superintendent at Cambridge. Improvement in the repair position, slow at first, rapidly gained impetus as one by one the old crocks were taken into Works to be replaced eventually by newly-repaired locomotives, besides a steady output of those locally reconditioned. From then on we did not look back and a repair figure usually within the target of 5% was consistently maintained. On one occasion it was as low as 3.14% much to the satisfaction of TCB and myself.

Another class of locomotive that engaged my attention was the little Intermediate LNER class E4 2–4–0 working then on numerous single line country branches. These little machines had acquired a reputation for poor steaming since the removal by the LNER of the hinged cap on the blastpipe for sharpening the blast. This was the invention of George McCallan, Works Manager at Stratford at the turn of the century, and extensively used by the GER. It was described at the time as a blast softener, and consisted of a hinged cap operated from the footplate, that could be lowered on to the blastpipe, reducing its orifice in the case of the E4s from 5½in to 5in. Unfortunately no compensating reduction in the size of the large orifice was made when the cap was discontinued, so many drivers resorted to the use of a 'jimmy' when in difficulty for steam. The jimmy, a device for sharpening the blast of a poor steaming locomotive, was probably as old as the steam locomotive itself – it took many forms, all of which were expressly forbidden. The most common was a length of tube cleaning rod, inserted into a tube in line with the blastpipe, tied or weighted down across the orifice, thereby splitting the exhaust into two jets and so increasing the area exposed to the entrainment of the gases of combustion. A blacksmith at March did quite a lucrative trade in manufacturing sets of jimmies of triangular section and varying widths, threaded like keys on a keyring, any one of which could be readily secured to or removed from a blast orifice by means of a thumb screw – there was much earnest debate among enginemen as to which position gave the best results, one placed lengthwise or one crosswise! The principle of increasing the area of entrainment by splitting the exhaust into a number of jets became accepted practice in later years, as witness the cruciform cowls of the Kylchap exhaust or the cruciform blast splitter fitted to many American locomotives.

Another less admirable method was to insert a stretcher bolt into the blast orifice. At Norwich one evening my attention was attracted by the heavy and laboured exhaust of a locomotive climbing Whitlingham bank on the Cromer line. I observed a Claud Hamilton 4–4–0 ejecting from its chimney a column of red-hot sparks and cinders more than 20ft high! When I examined this locomotive next morning I found a ⅞in bolt wedged across its 5⅛in blast orifice, thereby reducing its area by approximately one-fifth. No wonder that we were constantly receiving claims for compensation from lineside farmers for destruction of their crops – always wheat of the best quality! – caused by our fire-throwing locomotives. On one occasion, when making a spot check of smokeboxes, I even came across one link of a three-link coupling dropped down the blastpipe. Local alternatives to design such as the insertion of a ring into the blast orificie were also forbidden but, like the enginemen's jimmy, were resorted to on occasions when all else had failed, in order to avoid loss of time to trains. The wise man removed these unofficial aids to combustion before sending the locomotive to Works, to avoid embarrassing questions and to avoid having to manufacture the part or parts anew on the locomotive's return from shops, since all non-standard fittings were removed and thrown on the scrap heap as a matter of course.

To return to the E4s, it was obvious that a reduction in the size of the blast orifice would improve matters, and this I decided to try using the Swindon formula for a two-cylinder locomotive to determine its diameter, rather than the old rule-of-thumb – a quarter of the cylinder diameter, plus – viz:

$$\text{Diameter of Orifice} = \sqrt[4]{\frac{H}{70}}$$

where H = volume of one cylinder in cu in $\times \sqrt[4]{}$ evaporative (HS in sq ft) which gave an orifice $4^{11}/_{16}$in diameter. A ring was therefore prepared conical in shape internally for steadily contracting the orifice. Another school of thought, following Stroudley's practice on the LBSCR, favoured an internal lip at the orifice in order to spread the blast. An examination of *Gladstone*'s blast orifice revealed that it terminated abruptly in an internal lip amounting almost to a flange – yet another example of what E. S. Cox aptly described as unfinished business in exploring some of the lesser-known byways of locomotive design. Like most locomotives of the Victorian era, the E4 had a tall blastpipe, the distance between its tip and the chimney top being less than that considered necessary today for a proper ejector action by the column of exhaust steam. Accordingly, the pipe was reduced in height by 3in and a ring with a bore of $4^{11}/_{16}$in inserted. The result was most satisfactory and there were no more complaints of poor steaming. The same treatment was subsequently applied to the Norwich E4s with similar results. The porter bar for supporting the blastpipe while it was being cut down in the lathe was borrowed from Cambridge for this purpose. To the best of my knowledge all the E4s carried this modified blastpipe until their withdrawal from traffic under the modernisation programme. Looking back with the benefit of hindsight, I regret not having tried a Stroudley lip to make the blast fill the chimney at the top, as it might have saved shortening the pipe.

In the early 1920s there was a theory that chimneys should be designed with a taper of 1 in 6 to coincide with the general taper of a column of exhaust steam, and this led to the application of those hideous 'flowerpot' chimneys to many Great Central locomotives, completely spoiling their handsome appearance. Later research and experiences in South Africa confirmed the findings of the American test plants, that while the general taper of the exhaust column was 1 in 6, it expanded rapidly on leaving the orifice, equivalent to adding 80mm to its diameter, also the taper of the chimney from the choke upwards should be between 1 in 7 to 1 in 12; theoretically 1 in 6 was best, but the blastpipe height then became very critical.

A contributory factor to the poor steaming of the E4 Intermediates was the excessive amount of cold air drawn into the firebox when firing, with a consequent lowering of its temperature. The firehole door was of the standard GER pattern consisting of a circular plate hinged at footplate level that could be raised or lowered by means of a length of dog chain attached to the oven-door type of latch located on the driver's side of the footplate. Regulation of top air was achieved by dropping this latch into one of several notches in a small quadrant. The whole arrangement was simplicity itself and no doubt functioned admirably if the door were opened and closed by the driver between each shovelful, as intended by its Victorian designer. When there was not that co-operation between driver and fireman and the door was left open during firing, vast quantities of cold air were drawn in through the firehole which was 15in diameter. A remedy that I found in use in the Norwich district was the false door, a circular piece of ⅛in plate with an elliptical aperture at the bottom, just big enough for the blade of a firing shovel to pass through, that masked the firehole when the door was opened. There was a knack in adjusting the opening of the GER door for the admission of top air. It consisted in dropping the latch by means of its chain into the appropriate notch in the quadrant before the door was sucked shut by the vacuum created by the blast – to use the firemen's expression, they had to be 'fired on a short chain'.

There was probably no fitting on a locomotive that was used more frequently and took so many diverse forms than the firehole door. This and the injectors were the fittings that the fireman used most and his reactions to a foreign class of locomotive was largely influenced by the convenience of the former and reliability of the latter, considerations second only to its capacity to make steam. The types most common in British practice were the sliding double doors actuated by a single lever (GWR and LMS), a balanced trapdoor (LNER), an inward opening door hinged at its top that also serves as an air deflector (LNWR and NER) and more recently steam-operated butterfly doors of the Ajax pattern (SR).

Each type had its advocates, the first when lightly constructed so that it could be closed easily with one hand between shovelsful was probably the most popular for narrow firebox locomotives. The second type that could be opened with the tip of the shovel blade was the best in my experience for cutting-down the emission of heat when firing the back corners of a wide firebox locomotive. It also had an advantage from the management's point of view that unduly large lumps of coal could not be fired without first breaking them to a size small enough to pass through the trapdoor opening. Regarding the steam-operated butterfly door, some firemen were adept in its use, but the majority I have noticed operated the door manually for fear of getting their hands trapped and burnt should the door accidentally close when getting round the back corners of a wide firebox.

To return to my duties at Cambridge, a special responsibility of the mechanical foreman was the maintenance in first class condition of the Royal engine, always kept immaculately clean. Two-cylinder Class B2 4–6–0 No 1671 *Royal Sovereign*, rebuilt from a three-cylinder Class B17 locomotive by Edward Thompson was the principal Royal engine. Claud Hamilton 4–4–0 No 8763 resplendent in apple green with handrails and smokebox door ring brightly burnished was maintained in a similar condition at King's Lynn for working royal trains forward to Wolferton (the station for Sandringham). A change of locomotives was necessary because King's Lynn was a terminal station and the heavier locomotive was prohibited from working over this section of the route. Both locomotives were kept on local work in order to be available immediately when required. At that time the royal train was in frequent use by the Royal Family for its journeys to and from Sandringham and Newmarket. In all five locomotives were involved, Nos 1671 and 8783, one covering locomotive at King's Cross from whence the specials started, another at Cambridge, and a standby Claud Hamilton at King's Lynn.

Two days were normally required for the preparation of a royal engine, the first for washing-out the boiler, tube and firebox cleaning, and the replacement of any coal remaining in the tender by best quality Yorkshire hards from a wagon specially set aside for this purpose. The second day was spent in raising steam for proving the boiler joints, testing of brakes and injectors. Meanwhile the locomotive and tender, always kept clean even during the darkest days of the war, were given a special clean and all bright work polished. It was a great honour and a heavy responsibility, for no failure of a royal engine had occurred within living memory. This is not to say that every run was trouble-free, but thanks to the skill and enterprise of the crew and the presence of an HQ Inspector and a picked fitter who always accompanied the royal train, any difficulties experienced en route were overcome without loss of time.

Not so well organised were the odd occasions when a locomotive had to be provided to work a royal special, often at short notice, by depots not normally involved in working royal trains. I am reliably informed that on one occasion the only suitable engine available at a certain depot in the NE area was a very grimy and scruffy Class B1 4–6–0. As time was short and labour scarce, it was decided to concentrate on making a good job of cleaning the platform side of the locomotive rather than attempting to clean the whole. The dismay and chagrin can be imagined when at the last moment the royal train was diverted into another platform on the opposite side to the one planned!

At least twice during the twelve months that I was at Cambridge, No 1671 *Royal Sovereign* was sent to Stratford Works to have short cracks that had developed in the under edge of the main frame above the trailing bogie wheels – its weakest point – repaired by electric welding; the second visit resulted from a thermal crack adjacent to the first weld. As the B17s did not suffer from this weakness it seems reasonable to suspect that the cross-bracing that replaced the centre cylinder when this was removed was not strong enough to withstand the flexing imposed on the frames by increasing the diameter of the two outside cylinders from 17½in to 20in, and the load on the pistons by raising the boiler pressure from 180 lb/sq in to 225 lb/sq in when the B1 boiler was fitted. It should be explained that the B17 boiler was designed to carry the standard working pressure of 180 lb/sq in, but at some stage it was decided to increase this to 200 lb/sq in, possibly as a result of experience with the higher pressure boilers then being fitted to the Pacifics. While the B17 boiler had ample strength when new to withstand this increase in pressure, it was realised that the margin for wear and corrosion had been correspondingly reduced and that at some time in the future the pressure would have to be lowered to the original figure. This took place during the war when the older boilers were then fifteen years old.

Call out for the accident vans or breakdown train averaged one a week, ranging in importance from a wagon with one pair of wheels derailed in a siding, to a blockage of the main line. My chief recollection of this period is adopting a system of hand signals that I had first seen used by one surpervisor of the Newton Heath gang in Manchester for conveying my instructions to the driver of our 45 tons Cowans Sheldon breakdown crane, in preference to verbal commands. I had been most impressed by the speed and silence with which orders could be transmitted, and the almost complete elimination of those well-intentioned but superfluous shouted instructions to the crane driver by new and inexperienced members of the breakdown gang.

Prior to nationalisation it was common practice on the LNER when traffic was uni-directional as in colliery workings to balance power by returning locomotives to their starting points in convoys, often five at a time. At Gorton for example, the receipt of telegrams in code reading 'PIKE and OHIO all Langwith and Staveley engines', which when translated means 'Have search made for and send on all speed' etc., were of almost daily occurrence. Of the five locomotives in these convoys only the leading one was in steam, the others were dead, – the caretaker and a guard who rode on the last and middle locomotive respectively were both footplate men. The duty of the caretaker was to attend to the lubrication of the dead engines, those without mechanical lubrication to the cylinders being given a dose of oil down the blastpipe at intervals. An excellent rule originating on the GN stipulated that light engines could be depatched in one direction only on any given day, thus reducing the occupation of the line to a minimum. After nationalisation it became obligatory to take down the motion of any locomotive travelling dead for more than 25 miles, which effectively curbed the balancing of power by the older method.

The winter of 1946 was exceptionally hard, but it passed without incident at Cambridge, apart from a wagon of coal becoming jammed at the top of the wagon hoist type coaling plant when the platform to which it was secured came out of its guide rails. This entailed much heavy work at the top of ladders, in bitter conditions, to put right.

On 26 February 1947 I was appointed Locomotive Shed Master at Norwich, where I was instructed to report for duty on 3 March 1947.

(*left*) The oil dispensers at Norwich oil stores. (*right*) Some of the immaculate equipment racks in the Norwich stores.

Class B12 4–6–0 No 61572 near Stow Bedon on 16 May 1961. (*Dr Ian C. Allen*)

BR Standard Class 7 4–6–2 No 70007 at
Norwich in 1961, with centre driving
wheels removed – note Bulleid frame.
(*Dr Ian C. Allen*)

BR Standard Class 7 No 70013 *Oliver
Cromwell* en route to Bressingham
Steam Museum near Diss in Norfolk on
12 August 1968, after completing its last
workings for British Railways at the end
of steam operation the previous day.

The last steam locomotive at Norwich
motive power depot, Class J17 No 65567,
is seen departing on 31 March 1962.
(*Dr Ian C. Allen*)

CHAPTER 11

LOCOMOTIVE SHEDMASTER

Norwich locomotive depot, which until the early 1930s had been a subsidiary works to Stratford, I found to be a fascinating, rambling old place with many holes and corners, full of railway history and quite unlike any other depot at which I had worked or relieved. For example, the supply of water for locomotive needs was obtained from two tidal reservoirs or ponds fed by a short dyke from the River Wensum. Water flowed into the ponds on the flood tide and was retained by two self-closing circular hinged doors or flaps that prevented the impounded water escaping when the tide ebbed. The abundant natural supply was interrupted at roughly yearly intervals when a combination of southerly winds and neap tides reduced the period of high water to as little as 45 minutes. This phenomenon usually lasted about three days, by which time the water level dropped to such an extent that the 11,000-gallons storage tank could not be replenished. Conversely a combination of north westerly gales and spring tides caused widespread flooding, as it did in 1912 and again in 1953, when the sea walls were breached and vast areas of Norfolk inundated with salt water, including the well supplying the locomotive water tank of the M&GN at Stalham. As exceptionally low tides restricted the periods during which water flowed into the storage ponds, so did exceptionally high tides prevent the escape of water from the drains, thus causing flooding of the inspection pits, which became unusable at high water for a period of three days. The whole area on which the locomotive depot and station were built was very low lying, and water struck at a depth of 4ft; this created special problems with river pollution when diesel traction was introduced.

There is now a new maintenance depot near the electricity power station on ground formerly occupied by the Crown Point shunting yard. The 143-year-old depot near Thorpe Station is now disused. The long line of low buildings and the three road running shed to be seen on the left as a train enters Norwich are the original workshops of the Yarmouth & Norwich, later the Norfolk Railway, laid out in 1843 by William Prime Marshall, its first locomotive superintendent and a pupil and friend of Robert Stephenson who surveyed the route. Although used for offices their original purpose can be clearly seen from the four louvred ventilators in the slated roof below which were the brass and iron foundries. The fourth road in the running shed, which until 1949 retained its original pitched roof trussed with Memel pine, was the lifting shop, separated from the rest of the shed by a brick wall, in which at intervals there were flues and small fireplaces. These, I suggest, were not provided primarily for the comfort of the staff but were ventilating fires for the extraction of the noxious fumes from the coke, then the standard fuel for locomotives until the invention of the brick arch enabled coal to be burned without smoke in a locomotive firebox.

Beyond and parallel to the Norfolk Railway's workshop was a second row of much higher buildings. These were of GER origin, consisting of an erecting shop with eight transverse pits served by a 30-ton hand-operated gantry crane. Access to these pits through big double doors was by means of a traverser on the south side of the building. In the early 1930s the LNER altered this layout to two parallel roads when a wheel drop was installed, concurrently with plants for mechanical coaling and water softening.

In an easterly direction was the former boiler and blacksmiths' shop which had at one time fourteen smiths' forges. Two bricked-up doorways and two pairs of rails embedded in the shop floor indicated where boilers were brought into the shop on trolleys. There was, until the recent installation of fuel oil storage tanks, the truncated remains of the tall brick chimney serving the two Lancashire boilers supplying steam to a twin-cylinder vertical engine driving the shop machinery. Facing the boiler shop in a southerly direction was the former wagon repair shop now occupied by the Road Motor Department and served by numerous wagon turntables. Beyond this building and adjacent to the water storage reservoirs described earlier is the diesel railcar maintenance shop built in 1956 on ground formerly used for stacking coal, and known as Garden Lane.

Norwich had an allocation of 120 locomotives in 1947, including every type of GER tender locomotive other than the big J20 class 0–6–0s. The express passenger service was worked by the then newly-built B1 class mixed-traffic locomotives Nos 1040 to

1052 inclusive and the express freight trains to Whitemoor by ten K3 class three-cylinder machines, while the Claud Hamiltons had the monopoly of the local passenger services.

Norwich had been chosen by L. P. Parker as the pioneer depot for the introduction of his Planned Servicing Scheme of locomotive maintenance and my first task was to put this into operation. It was dated 31 May 1948 and was as follows:

THE PLANNED SERVICING SYSTEM

Introduction

The reason for our existence as locomotive running people is, in the operating sense, to provide power to work whatever traffics have been offered in the most economical and efficient way possible. Economy can only be achieved by the maximum use of available equipment and efficiency by the maintenance of that equipment in such a condition as will enable it to do the work for which it was designed. The number of engines to maintain in traffic in relation to our total stock and the amount of time they are maintained in traffic in relation to the total time available are measures of our economy. The number of trains worked punctually and correctly in relation to the total number of trains worked is the measure of our efficiency.

All equipment which does work must deteriorate and some period between turns of duty in which the deterioration may be made good is essential but to obtain the economy just defined the number and duration of those periods must be kept to a minimum. The faults which have developed must, in consequence, be rectified speedily and, more important still, the amount and extent of these faults must also be kept to a minimum.

From the foregoing, therefore, emerge a number of basic principles upon which any sound system of servicing locomotives must be based:

(a) The diagrammed time available between spells of duty must be such as will enable all servicing work to be done without the need for additional periods out of traffic to make good arrears. Operating conditions almost invariably give this time – and more – provided that we apply correctly the principles which follow.

(b) To make the best use of this time very careful attention must be paid to having the right amount of people armed with the right amount of material, the right amount of knowledge and with the right tools in the right place at the right time.

(c) To reduce the work which those people have to do to the minimum preventive rather than curative methods of maintenance must be adopted.

It is around these three simple principles that the Planned Servicing system has been created and applied in the Eastern Section. The servicing and maintenance schedules which are an important part of the system have been adapted by, and are now in use in the Western Section under the name of the Shed Servicing Scheme.

The yardstick by which a depot's efficiency in maintaining its motive power was measured was the percentage of its locomotives daily available for traffic and the generally accepted achievable optimum was 85 per cent. Provided that a locomotive had been at work for some part of the 24 hours (even if only for a few minutes) it was shown legitimately as at work for that day. For example, a locomotive coming off a train arriving a few minutes after midnight could be cooled-down, washed-out, repairs executed and be back in steam the same day in time to work the 23.35 hours Haughley mail.

Of the remaining fifteen percent it could be assumed that (a) 5% would be in Main Works, (b) 5% under examination or depot repair including collision damage and hot axleboxes, (c) 2% would be waiting material, and (d) 3% available by 6.00pm after boiler washing or repair, but for which no suitable work could be found. The shedmaster was solely responsible for items (b), (c) and (d) but had little control over (c) beyond anticipating his future needs and ordering material well in advance. The same remark applied also to (a) as it was the Shopping Bureau which from the shopping proposals submitted decided which locomotives should be called into works. One no longer fit to work would appear on the stop list as waiting Works. The depot master's aim was to see that not more than 10 per cent of his allocation was stopped at any one time. Naturally this was easier to achieve at a large depot than at a small one and that is why the district shed or concentration depot undertook the major examinations of locomotives allocated to its sub-sheds.

The three per cent figure for locomotives released but not used was not introduced until mid-1949; prior to this date the target was seven per cent and this fact must be borne in mind when comparing one year's figures with another. The average annual percentage of Norwich locomotives not available for work during the eleven years 1947 to 1957 when, with a change of organisation these statistics ceased, were shown opposite.

Works and staff holidays during the summer and sickness during the winter, a run of hot axleboxes or a major overhaul, are all reflected by the number of locomotives under repair.

Year	Average Annual %	Worst Individual Figure	Target %
1947	10.10	16.80	7.00
1948	6.40	10.70	7.00
1949	8.50	11.50	7.00
1949	10.30	12.50	10.00
1950	10.00	15.30	10.00
1951	10.30	14.30	10.00
1952	10.75	14.60	10.00
1953	11.05	14.60	10.00
1954	9.05	12.90	10.00
1955	8.55	13.40	10.00
1956	10.60	14.70	10.00
1957	11.20	*18.80	10.00

*Waiting material

The graph for 1952 illustrates what a sensitive indicator the locomotive availability return is:

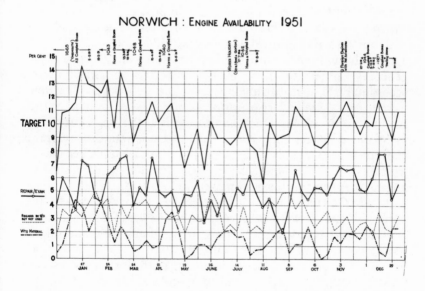

NORWICH : ENGINE AVAILABILITY 1951

The next stage of reorganising the procedure for locomotive maintenance initiated by L. P. Parker was the introduction of a logical method of calculating the number of fitters necessary to maintain any specific type in order that anomalies in staffing between depots should be removed. The accurate records of man-hours expended at the PSS shed day on various classes now made this possible. I was given the task of working out a points value for each class, taking as my unit of comparison the small GER six-coupled goods engine (LNER class J15) long renowned for its simplicity and lightness on repairs. Most railways had similar examples. One that comes immediately to mind is the Ivatt large Atlantic of the GNR, of which was said that it required little beyond a supply of coal, water and oil to keep it going.

On G. A. Musgrave's retirement LPP had become responsible for all motive power depots in the Eastern Region and maintenance points had now to be awarded to former Great Central and Great Northern locomotives and those LNER classes of which we had little or no experience on the Great Eastern line.

This proved to be a most interesting task and gave me the added pleasure of working once again with Herbert Bell, a colleague of my days at Gerrards Cross, and by then Assistant District Running Superintendent at Gorton. The method adopted was first to canvas the mechanical foremen at the principal depots on the GN and GC sections for their opinions, often diverse as to which classes gave the most trouble to maintain. These, combined with our own practical experience and judgement enabled us to equate the unknown with the known, ie locomotives of types generally similar to those in the PSS and to award points accordingly. It soon became apparent that if awkward fractions were to be avoided a larger unit than one was needed and a scale ranging from 10 for small tank engines, the easiest type to maintain, to 30 for the Class U1 Garratt was found to be more convenient. Under this scheme the J15 (the base unit) became 13 which enabled the other classes to be graded with reasonable accuracy. A copy of this grading schedule is given.

Re-assessment of a few individual classes was made at the request of one or two district officers but in the main the grading was accepted as realistic; the only major alteration made was to reduce the value of the basic unit from 10 to 3, which resulted in fewer and therefore coarser gradations. With this arrangement a Class J15 equalled 3, a B1 equalled 6, and a BR Class 7 Britannia 4–6–2 equalled 7 points.

The LNER classification which was a development of the old GNR system allotted a letter of the alphabet to each wheel arrangement and once the code has been learned the type of locomotive was quickly identified.

The figures following the letter indicate the locomotive's origin generally in the order GN, GC, GE, NE, NB, GNS, but as classes

Schedule 2 – Classes in order of units
Shed days at two-week intervals.
Range of units 10 to 30. Class J15 = 13

Unit	Classes
10	G5 (push-and-pull), J62, J63, J72, J94
11	F2, F4, F5, F6
12	J65, J66, J67, J68, J69, Y3
13	J15, H2, N4, N5
15	C1, C4, C13, E4, F6, J17, J70, Y4, Y5
17	D1, D2, D3, J1, J2, J3, J4, J5, J10, J11
20	B1, B2, B4, B5, C13, C14, D9, D10, D11, D15, D16, J19, J20, J30, K1, K2, K5, L1, N1, O1, O4, Q1, Q4, V1, V3
22	A1, A3, A4, A10, J6, W1, V2
24	A2, A5, B12, J39, K3, L3, N2, N7, O7
26	O3
28	B17, S1
30	B7, O2, U1

Letter	Wheel arrangement	Letter	Wheel arrangement	Letter	Wheel arrangement	Letter	Wheel arrangement
A	4-6-2	G	0-4-4	N	0-6-2	T	4-8-0
B	4-6-0	H	4-4-4	O	2-8-0	U	2-8-0+0-8-2
C	4-4-2	J	0-6-0	P	2-8-2	V	2-6-2
D	4-4-0	K	2-6-0	Q	0-8-0	W	4-6-4
E	2-4-0	L	2-6-4	R	0-8-2	Y	0-4-0
F	2-4-2	M	0-6-4	S	0-8-4	Z	0-4-2

became extinct there were gaps. For example, when the LNER was formed in 1923 most of its constituent companies possessed examples of the once ubiquitous 0-4-4 suburban tank, yet at nationalisation only those of the North Eastern (G5) and Great North of Scotland (G10) remained.

Applying the maintenance formula to a depot with six Britannias, fourteen B1s and eighteen J15s and the number of fitters needed to maintain that fleet would be calculated as follows:

6 Britannias	@	7 units	=	42
14 B1s	@	6 units	=	84
18 J15s	@	3 units	=	54
		Total	=	180 points

Five per cent was then deducted from this total on account of locomotives in main works and the result divided by the points value for the number of J15s that one fitter was capable of maintaining, to which was added a small allowance for contingencies viz $\dfrac{180\times95}{19\times100}=$ 9 fitters or just over 4 locomotives per man. Ten years' experience with the points system of evaluation proved it to be practical and equitable.

Returning to the early spring of 1947, after this initial preoccupation with implementing the Planned Servicing Schemes, I had time to reflect on my position in the organisation at Norwich as it then existed, and this was in many respects far from satisfactory. When, following North Eastern Railway practice, Edward Thompson created the post of locomotive shedmaster at the principal sheds, he seemed to have overlooked the fact that whereas on the NER the district locomotive superintendent and his staff had their offices in the town away from the shed, in the southern area of the LNER these offices were located at the principal shed, for the running of which the Assistant Locomotive Superintendent was responsible. I was therefore in effect a supernumerary grafted onto the existing organisation with responsibility, but for a while little real authority. I hasten to add that this was no fault of my old friend Ted Lindop, the ALS, who assisted me in every possible way to take over the running of the depot. For quite a long time staff seeking an audience with the man in charge continued to knock on his office door and very few on mine, such is the Norfolkman's dislike of change and reluctance to accept a foreigner until proved worthy of his trust.

The introduction in this post-war period of rest days for footplate and conciliation grades consequent on the reduction of the 48-hour working week to an 88-hour fortnight in the first stage followed in the next by a 40-hour week with a weekly rest day, led to a proportional increase in staff. Twenty additional shedmen to cover rest day relief for such grades as boiler washers, steam raisers, tube cleaners and so on were recruited mainly from men returning from HM Forces. Some of these new faces that I saw about the premises on a Monday morning I did not recognise as having interviewed and it was then that I discovered to my dismay that a grade 4 female clerk was interviewing and engaging applicants to fill vacancies without reference to me or any one else in authority. A sharp exchange of views with the chief staff clerk followed this discovery, when I reminded him that the selection of staff was my responsibility and if, as he asserted, I could not be found when wanted because I was either under an engine or about the yard, then an interview at a later date must be arranged. Thereafter all applicants were seen by me and I took great trouble over their selection, as once engaged they had every prospect of 45 years' service ahead of them. Unfortunately, I was saddled with those previously engaged among whom were several undesirable characters.

It was not until the formation of the traffic manager's organisation early in 1958, when the district officer and his staff removed to new premises near the station, that I really became a shedmaster in my own right, holding my own Local Departmental Committee and Workshop Committee meetings with the staff who had now but one master to please. Consequently our relationship became much closer and more harmonious.

In the meantime like others before me I had fallen under the spell of Norwich, which has been described by some as the graveyard of ambition, for I decided that it was here that I wanted to stay. Where else could I find a depot of its size and importance that caused so little worry to run yet was within walking distance of the pleasant riverside village of Thorpe St Andrew where I had made my home? I have never regretted that decision which enabled me to keep in constant touch with the realities of locomotive maintenance and the teamwork necessary to run a large depot – all aspects of railway work that I most enjoy.

To revert to 1947, steel rationing was then still in force and there were no fewer than twelve speed restrictions in the 45 miles between Norwich and Ipswich, while speed throughout the line was limited to a maximum of 60mph due to a shortage of new rails. Coal, or rather its erratic supply, was my principal headache and continued to be so for the next three years or more. The shortfall in our weekly consumption of 1,800 tons was met by lifting from our storage stacks, which when walled and filled to capacity contained 4,300 tons. These had to be replenished at intervals, and depending on whether there was a shortage or a surplus on any particular day we were either picking up or putting down coal. Casual labourers or German prisoners of war were employed on this duty and I recorded that on a Sunday in August 1947 thirty German POWs loaded 140 tons of coal into sixteen wagons in five-and-a-half hours and on the day following, 26 casual labourers

took eight hours to fill eleven wagons with 107 tons – a poor
performance when compared with that of the two men coaling
locomotives at Rickmansworth, who regularly shifted 20 tons
apiece. Even this low rate of lifting could not be kept up when the
distance from the coal face to the wagon increased, necessitating
the use of wheelbarrows.

A highlift mechanical shovel and its operator were then hired
but this proved a disappointment as it pushed the coal away in
front of it. An RB10 excavator equipped with a heavy bucket or
grab and a long jib that reached to the middle of the stack was then
tried and proved to be a much better proposition, by filling 209
wagons in fourteen days each of twelve hours. The final
development used when rebuilding the stack was to mount this
excavator on a rail flat wagon, so that it could run the whole length
of the stack, emptying wagons standing on an adjacent road as it
went along; it also allowed the operator to see better what he was
doing.

During this period of uncertainty with coal supplies, it was
agreed that we should accept 8.9 per cent of our fuel in the shape of
Cardiff briquettes. These were unpopular with both the coalman
and enginemen on account of the fumes of ammonia that were
released when broken-up, which made the eyes bloodshot, smart,
and water. There was a near riot on one occasion when through a
shunter's negligence the day's intake of loco coal was found to
consist entirely of briquettes!

At this period we received supplies of coal from Poland,
Belgium, the USA (Pennsylvania) and France (Pas de Calais) as
well as an increasing amount for opencast workings in this
country. We also received a few wagons of house coal which burnt
swiftly and made an enormous amount of black smoke, while at
home we crouched over fires of what people called slate or rock –
that was in fact excellent steam coal when consumed in its proper
place, a locomotive firebox. The quality of the coal as measured by
its ash content continued to decline as its price increased, both
prime factors leading within a decade to the replacement of the
steam locomotive by diesel-electric power.

	1939	1943	1948	1958
Ash content (%)	5.20	6.60	7.70	—
Price per ton (£)	0.90	—	2.30	5.00

The last published figures gave the price of locomotive coal at the pithead as £5.00 per ton
and railway diesel fuel oil as 5p per gallon.

A Britannia class steam locomotive hauling a nine-coach train from Norwich to London and back (230 miles) consumed approximately four tons of coal for the round trip at a cost of £20 compared with £11.50 for an English Electric 2000hp diesel-electric locomotive which on the same duty, consumed one gallon of fuel oil per mile. The relative calorific value of the two fuels was 12,600BTU for Blidworth coal and 19,000BTU for gas oil.

October 1947 was memorable for a series of trials carried out on the Colchester main line with the NER dynamometer car and its team of four test engineers under the supervision of D. R. Carling, for the purpose of establishing which of two locomotives, identical in every respect apart from the number of cylinders, was best suited for the service. The two were class B17 No 1622, with three 17½in diameter cylinders and No 1607, rebuilt as Class B2 by Edward Thompson with two 20in diameter cylinders. Both types had a common stroke of 26in and boilers pressed to 225 lb/sq in. I was privileged to ride in the dynamometer car when No 1622 was being tested with a trailing load of 313 tons including the dynamometer car on the 10.10am semi-fast train to London, returning with the 3.40pm express. A peak figure of 1,050 drawbar horse-power was exerted in lifting the train out of the Stour valley, up the two-and-a-half miles of Dedham bank, which has a gradient of 1 in 134. Below are consecutive readings to the summit followed, by those on the descent through Ardleigh:

Time	Boiler pressure lb/sq.in	Steamchest pressure lb/sq.in	Smokebox vacuum in/water	Blastpipe pressure lb/sq.in	Regulator	Cut-off%	Drawbar pull tons	DPHP	Speed mph
12.01	215	200	3½	3¾	Full	46	4½–5		
12.01	215	200	4⅜	4¼	Full	46		900	20
12.02	220	200	5½	5¾	Full	46			25
12.02½	220	200	6	6¾	Full	40	5½	950	25
12.04	220	200	5⅝	5⅜	Full	40	5	1,000	
12.04	225	215	5⅜	4¾	Full	36		1,050	35
12.05	225	215	5½	4⅞	Full	36	4½		
12.05	225	215				24	3½		
12.05	225	215				15	2¾		
12.06½	225	220	1¾	1	Full	10	2		56

On the return journey with the 3.40pm down the following readings were recorded when ascending Brentwood bank at its steepest inclination of 1 in 85:

Time	Boiler pressure lb/sq.in	Steamchest pressure lb/sq.in	Smokebox vacuum in/water	Blastpipe pressure lb/sq.in	Regulator	Cut-off %	Drawbar pull tons	DPHP	Speed mph
16.08	230*	225	3⅜	2¾	Full	24	3½		30

*A fault had developed in the pressure gauge, causing it to read 5lb heavy.

New Year's day 1948, traditionally ushered in with much blowing of whistles, saw the start of a new era, the long-awaited nationalisation of the nation's transport system. Each mode of transport was to carry the traffic for which it was best suited, to avoid wasteful competition. Executive committees were set up for the control and co-ordination of the railways, buses, road transport of goods, canals and coastwise shipping. This laudable objective did not survive long, due to frequent changes in policy made by successive governments. No one today attempting a cross-country journey by rail and bus would think that such a policy had ever existed.

The reaction of railwaymen to this change from private to public ownership varied considerably. Some who took their leaders' boast that 'We are the masters now!' were frankly disappointed that their local bosses were still the same ones with whom they had negotiated and contended for years past, but the majority welcomed the change for they felt initially at least that now they were working for the common good.

Management had become accustomed to government control through the Railway Executive Committee during the war. As in the composition of that body representatives of the LMS company predominated, it came as no surprise that where there was little to choose between one company's practice and another LMS methods and standards should be adopted. This we accepted philosophically, having gone through the same throes of unification following the amalgamation of the railways into four groups in 1923. Now twenty-five years later we were to begin again. Having during the interim fitted every LNER locomotive with standard 11TPI boiler stays, washout and fusible plugs and pipe unions, these had now to be altered to the rate of 12 threads per inch, so that for many years or the life of a firebox there would be two standards in force, with the attendant risks.

The first outward and visible sign of nationalisation was the appearance on locomotives of the new title BRITISH RAILWAYS, hand-painted in full, mainly on Sundays at double time rates, when there were the most locomotives in the sheds. This was soon replaced by a transfer crest depicting a wheel surmounted by a stylised lion (popularly referred to as the 'emasculated weasel' 'cat and cartwheel' and similar expressions) which in its turn was superseded by a more dignified emblem, this time a wheel held by a lion.

Whole trains in experimental liveries on which the public were asked to express their preference, the plum and spilt milk of the old LNWR and brown and cream of the GWR, began to tour the country. The larger express engines were painted Caledonian blue, lined out in black and white; this did not look too bad on the Gresley Pacifics but was ill-suited to the abundance of polished brass and copper on Great Western locomotives. In my opinion it gave them a garish fairground appearance, whereas they were shown up to advantage by the handsome Brunswick green livery, just as the only adornment suited to the light apple green of the LNER was polished steel. The livery finally adopted for BR steam was plain black for goods locomotives, black lined-out in LNWR style for mixed traffic passenger locomotives, except selected classes which were painted a slightly lighter shade of GWR green. These colours combined well with coaches in either the earlier crimson and cream or later plain maroon lake livery which wore well and did not look so dingy or sombre as the dark green almost universal on the Continent at that time.

The most interesting and exciting event of 1948 was undoubtedly the exhaustive series of dynamometer car trials carried out during the summer over selected routes throughout the country with representative types of express passenger, mixed-traffic and heavy freight locomotives from each Region. This was to ascertain their performance over routes with physical characteristics differing widely from those for which they had been specifically designed, with a view to embodying the best features of each in the proposed new standard range of

Comparative Coal and Water Rates during the 1948 Locomotive Exchanges

COAL CONSUMPTION AND COMPARATIVE PERCENTAGES

Region / Locomotive class / Lb. of coal per hr. / DHP		1 Eastern "A.4" 3·06	2 L. Midland "Duchess" 3·12	3 Eastern "O.1" 3·37	4 L. Midland "6.P" 3·38	5 Western "28 X X" 3·42	6 L. Midland "8.F" 3·52	7 Ex W.D. 2-10-0 3·52	8 L. Midland "5" 3·54	9 Western "King" 3·57	10 Eastern "B.1" 3·59	11 Southern "M.N." 3·60	12 Ex W.D. 2-8-0 3·77	13 Western "Hall" 3·94	14 Southern "W. C't'y" 4·11
Eastern, "A.4"	4-6-2	—	1·96	10·15	10·46	11·77	15·05	15·05	15·70	16·68	17·35	17·66	23·25	28·80	34·38
L. Midland, "Duchess"	4-6-2	1·93	—	8·02	8·34	9·62	12·83	12·83	13·46	14·45	15·08	15·40	20·87	26·31	31·80
Eastern, "O.1"	2-8-0	9·18	7·41	—	0·30	1·49	4·45	4·45	5·04	5·93	6·53	6·83	11·87	16·92	21·90
L. Midland, "6.P"	4-6-0	9·47	7·68	0·30	—	1·19	4·14	4·14	4·73	5·62	6·22	6·51	11·55	16·58	21·60
Western, "28 X X"	2-8-0	10·54	8·77	1·46	1·17	—	2·93	2·93	3·51	4·38	4·98	5·26	10·25	15·22	20·20
L. Midland, "8.F"	2-8-0	13·07	11·37	4·26	3·97	2·84	—	—	0·57	1·42	1·99	2·27	7·10	11·93	16·76
Ex W.D.	2-10-0	13·07	11·37	4·26	3·97	2·84	—	—	0·57	1·42	1·99	2·27	7·10	11·93	16·76
L. Midland, "5"	4-6-0	13·57	11·87	4·80	4·52	3·39	0·56	0·56	—	0·85	1·42	1·70	6·50	11·30	16·10
Western, "King"	4-6-0	14·30	12·60	5·59	5·32	4·20	1·40	1·40	0·84	—	0·56	0·84	5·60	10·37	15·15
Eastern, "B.1"	4-6-0	14·76	13·10	6·13	5·85	4·73	1·95	1·95	1·40	0·56	—	0·28	5·02	9·75	14·50
Southern, "Merchant Navy"	4-6-2	15·00	13·35	6·38	6·11	4·99	2·22	2·22	1·67	0·83	0·28	—	4·73	9·43	14·18
Ex W.D.	2-8-0	18·85	17·25	10·61	10·35	9·28	6·63	6·63	6·10	5·31	4·78	4·52	—	4·52	9·02
Western, "Hall"	4-6-0	22·35	20·85	14·48	14·23	13·20	10·67	10·67	9·87	9·38	8·88	8·63	4·32	—	4·32
Southern, "West Country"	4-6-2	25·57	24·10	18·05	17·79	16·82	14·37	14·37	13·89	13·16	12·67	12·43	8·28	4·14	—

WATER CONSUMPTION AND COMPARATIVE PERCENTAGES

Region / Locomotive class / Lb. of water per hr. / DHP		1 Eastern "A.4" 24·32	2 Eastern "O.1" 25·73	3 L. Midland "6.P" 25·81	4 Western "28 X X" 26·80	5 L. Midland "Duchess" 27·08	6 L. Midland "8.F" 27·26	7 Eastern "8.1" 27·64	8 L. Midland "5" 27·99	9 Ex W.D. 2-10-0 28·05	10 Western "King" 28·58	11 Ex W.D. 2-8-0 28·75	12 Western "Hall" 29·97	13 Southern "M.N." 30·43	14 Southern "W. C't'y" 32·64
Eastern, "A.4"	4-6-2	—	5·79	6·13	10·22	11·36	12·10	13·66	15·11	15·36	17·52	18·25	23·30	25·15	34·25
Eastern, "O.1"	2-8-0	5·48	—	0·31	4·16	5·24	5·94	7·42	8·78	9·02	11·08	11·74	16·50	18·26	26·90
L. Midland, "6.P"	4-6-0	5·77	0·31	—	3·84	4·92	5·62	7·08	8·44	8·68	10·74	11·40	16·13	17·90	26·50
Western, "28 X X"	2-8-0	9·25	3·99	3·70	—	1·05	1·73	3·16	4·48	4·70	6·68	7·33	11·93	13·66	22·00
L. Midland, "Duchess"	4-6-2	10·20	4·98	4·68	1·03	—	0·67	2·07	3·36	3·58	5·54	6·17	10·68	12·38	20·52
L. Midland, "8.F"	2-8-0	10·80	5·62	5·32	1·69	0·66	—	1·40	2·68	2·90	4·84	5·47	9·94	11·64	19·50
Eastern, "8.1"	4-6-0	12·03	6·90	6·62	3·04	2·03	1·38	—	1·27	1·49	3·40	4·02	8·43	10·10	18·10
L. Midland, "5"	4-6-0	13·13	8·08	7·78	4·25	3·25	2·61	1·25	—	0·22	2·11	2·72	7·07	8·71	16·62
Ex W.D.	2-10-0	13·32	8·27	7·98	4·46	3·47	2·82	1·46	0·21	—	1·89	2·50	6·84	8·48	16·40
Western, "King"	4-6-0	14·77	9·87	9·59	6·17	5·20	4·57	3·26	2·05	1·84	—	0·60	4·86	6·47	14·20
Ex W.D.	2-8-0	15·38	10·46	10·19	6·75	5·78	5·16	3·84	2·63	2·43	0·59	—	4·24	5·84	13·55
Western, "Hall"	4-6-0	18·68	14·16	13·90	10·59	9·64	9·04	7·78	6·60	6·40	4·63	4·07	—	1·54	8·90
Southern, "Merchant Navy"	4-6-2	20·10	15·45	15·17	11·93	11·02	10·42	9·16	8·02	7·83	6·08	5·52	1·53	—	7·25
Southern, "West Country"	4-6-2	25·50	21·20	20·92	17·90	17·08	16·49	15·35	14·25	14·08	12·44	11·93	8·17	6·77	—

Method of use : Select locomotive in VERTICAL columns 1-14. Find locomotive for comparison in LEFT hand column. The figure in VERTICAL column on SAME line as the comparison locomotive is the percentage by which the locomotive in columns 1-14 differs from locomotive in LEFT hand column. LIGHT figures are INCREASES. BOLD figures are DECREASES

locomotives. The result of these trials, their analysis and the conclusions drawn from them is contained in the 130-page *Official Report of the Locomotive Testing Committee on the Locomotive Exchange Trials* of 1948, to which the student of locomotive design is referred. The late Cecil J. Allen's two admirable books *The Locomotive Exchanges* and its sequel *New Light on the Locomotive Exchanges* written after the release of the official report are also recommended reading. For the general reader an interesting table by which the coal and water consumption of any one class of locomotive can be compared with that of its rival is given above by kind permission of the editor of *The Railway Gazette*.

A word of caution is necessary however when comparing the performance of one locomotive with another. There was no uniformity in the method of driving – some drivers would make up time lost by signal checks and other delays, while others considered that they had fulfilled their duty by keeping strictly to sectional times, thereby saving coal. For example, the performance of the LMS Duchess in climbing hills was consistently far below what these locomotives were capable of achieving, whereas the power output of the Southern's West

Country class No 34004 *Yeovil* on the Highland line was so terrific that in climbing the three-mile 1 in 80 gradient from Blair Athol, it nearly halved the scheduled time and winded the banking engine attached to assist it! It gave me great satisfaction to see a Gresley A4 Pacific chosen to represent the LNER. Its consistently good performance put it at the top of the locomotive league table despite the trouble experienced on three occasions with a heated middle big-end.

The last express passenger locomotive designed specifically for the Great Eastern lines was the three-cylinder B17 class, introduced in 1928. Norwich had the distinction of possessing the two streamlined examples, No 2859 *East Anglian* and No 2870 *City of London,* which before World War II were employed exclusively on the prestige East Anglican expresses. These were supplemented during the early 1930s by the rebuilding of the GER 1500 class with larger diameter round-top boilers and long-travel valves.

In 1948 both types began to be replaced by Edward Thompson's B1 class mixed-traffic 4–6–0s designed to have as wide a route availability as possible. These had an excellent front end arrangement and soon proved themselves capable of running the fast express trains in East Anglia without the slightest difficulty. Unfortunately they lacked robustness and due to the need to pare weight down to a minimum their coupled axleboxes were made smaller than was desirable; the reciprocating balance was cut down to 36% in order to reduce rail hammerblow. These factors combined with an absence of axlebox wedges to take up wear resulted in an early deterioration of their riding qualities.

After running anything from 40,000 to 70,000 miles on express work, drivers began to complain that their locomotives were no longer fit to ride upon, due to the vibration set up by coupled axleboxes knocking like a steam hammer. No 1041 was practically bad in this respect, producing when running at speed with steam shut off a sickening vibration of high frequency. For that reason it was never regularly manned like the other B1s, but was kept as the spare engine – by contrast No 1045 was considered to ride better than the rest. The trouble peculiar to No 1041 was eventually traced to an over-balance of 60 lb in each of the driving wheels when these were put in the wheel balancing machine in Doncaster Works after the Works Mechanical Inspector had been persuaded to ride on the locomotive.

Deterioration in the riding of the B1s developed earlier still after their first general repair in Stratford Works, generally around 40,000–50,000 miles, and it soon became evident that the hornblocks were not being reconditioned to an acceptable standard. Consequent on complaints from the districts regarding the quality of Stratford repairs, it was arranged that each shedmaster should visit Stratford Works periodically to see for himself how his locomotives were being repaired. Considerable tact and diplomacy (not always exercised) was necessary during these visits. My own experience was that the repair process that I had come to see, either had not been started or else had been completed. I formed the opinion that the facilties for reconditioning hornblocks were inadequate, for I saw no such machine as that used at Darlington resembling a port facing machine with multiple heads for machining parallel the horn faces. As a result, I devised a method of measuring the total or cumulative knock, ie wear in the horns plus crown roll in the bore of an axlebox of a locomotive in steam by setting the big-end of the side being tested at the bottom, scotching the driving wheels securely and then applying steam first to one side of the piston and then the other, marking on the frame with a special trammel located in the wheel centre the amount that the frame moved relative to the axle. The following readings taken from B1 4–6–0 No 1041 are fairly representative

Axle	Left-hand	Right-hand
Leading	3/64in	1/16in
Driving	9/64in	9/64in
Trailing	1/16in	1/8in

To return to 1947, reconditioning the trailing coupled axleboxes which had proved adequate with the B17s was of no avail on the B1s because the axlebox guides or hornblocks had worn wider at the top than at the bottom; a fault which in those with wedge adjustment can be corrected by machining the wedge to bring it once more parallel with the fixed horn face. Those without wedges can be corrected at a running shed only by filing or hand grinding, a long and slow process.

I was now faced with a dilemma common to most running men – what to do with locomotives so rough that in order to keep time their crews were caused considerable discomfort and which shops would not accept for repair because they had not run the 100,000 miles expected from a new locomotive? The answer was to undertake at Norwich what amounted to intermediate repairs at the expense of neglecting other and less imperative work.

In this I was guided by the principles of the Planned Servicing System by doing only such work as was really necessary. 'Do you pull up the plants in your garden every few weeks in order to see how their roots are growing? Then why keep taking an engine apart just to measure wear when its condition can be ascertained by testing in steam?' This advice I took literally and valves and pistons proved steamtight at the fortnightly steam test were allowed to run until they gave an indication that the rings needed changing. Some classes would run nearly double the scheduled mileage before needing attention and the labour thus saved was diverted to the more important work of overhauling the B1s.

The tradition that it had once been a main works lingered on at Norwich and soon large squares, straight edges, surface plates and trammels appeared from long-forgotten hiding places and the work of rectifying axleboxes and hornchecks started in earnest, substituting a cup grinder for the three-square file of former days and this made the task of trueing-up the horns quicker and easier. The surface plate was next applied and the high spots that it revealed removed with a diamond-pointed scraper made from a chisel bar. Meanwhile, new bronze axleboxes were being planed to size ready for trying-up the leading and driving horns (in which they should just hold by their own weight) preparatory to marking-off for boring. The trailing axleboxes of cast steel were also having new boss and side liners attached and new crown brasses pressed in. After boring and bedding on the axleboxes to their journals with blue marking, the wheels were replaced temporarily under the locomotive, which was given a dry run up and down the yard before dropping the wheels again to make sure that the boxes were resting squarely on their journals. This was an excellent practice that I had not encountered elsewhere, but which on those classes of locomotives with collars on their axles did much to eliminate a subsequent heating. Records were kept of the number of times an axlebox had to be applied to its journal to give a good bearing, and thus was found to be 2.45 times if the journal had been turned and 4.46 times when it had not. An opportunity was taken while the wheels were out for turning to recondition as necessary axle journals, tender axlebox brasses and piston rods, to re-bush coupling and connecting rods; re-metal crossheads, renew valve and piston rings and run out the bogie for examination. Later batches of B1s were provided, I believe, with axlebox liners of manganese steel, thus eliminating the need to reface horns on account of wear. My detailed report on these matters appears at the end of this chapter.

Several unusual and interesting repairs were undertaken at Norwich in 1947, such as removing from its frame the loose left-hand cylinder of a K2 class 2–6–0 in order to renew the sheet copper exhaust joint or gasket, reamer out the cylinder bolt holes and turn new driving fit bolts. This locomotive had seen long service in Scotland, where presumably as a war economy measure shear strips butting up closely to the cylinder flanges had been electrically welded to the frame in an attempt to stop the cylinder from moving. K2 No 1742, reported badly off the beat, was found to have in its left-hand cylinder (recently renewed) not only valve liners of a wrong pattern but also odd valve heads, one being almost $\frac{1}{2}$in wider than the other. The combined effect of all these errors was to give the valves an exhaust clearance of no less than $\frac{7}{8}$in, thus allowing high-pressure steam to escape before it had fully expanded. To the best of my recollection the odd valve head was changed for one of the correct pattern and both valve heads spaced further apart on their spindle in order to give the correct exhaust clearance and a steam distribution approximating to that of the right-hand cylinder.

Another valve liner problem of a quite different kind arose in the autumn of 1948 when the second batch of B1s, Nos 1270–2, began to give trouble with valve rings breaking. Investigation revealed that the valve liners had been made from too soft an iron, so causing the narrow port bars to wear away rapidly and develop deep ridges that broke the rings. In the case of No 1270 wear had increased the diameter of the liner at the port bars by $\frac{1}{8}$in. A campaign of valve liner renewal followed this discovery, Stratford Works supplying a drilling jig and a specially long $\frac{5}{8}$in drill to enable two parallel holes to be drilled close together down the length of the liner in order to collapse it. New liners of hard iron skimmed on the outside to a nice fit were then pulled into the steamchest with a fine thread drawbolt – an intermediate stage between the old-fashioned method of expanding the steam chest by heating with gas jets and the modern practice of shrinking a liner by freezing.

During the summer of 1948 several of the earlier B1s failed with their piston rods breaking at the crosshead cone end. These included No 1041 at Ipswich on 9 July, No 1044 at Chelmsford and No 1050 at Norwich. Examination of the remainder revealed several instances of tool marks from which cracks could originate and poor workmanship in fitting the rod into its crosshead. As no trouble was subsequently experienced with broken piston rods after these had been renewed, these failures could be fairly attributed to poor workmanship and possibly defective material.

Understandably during these early days of nationalisation it had been a case of 'business as usual', but now the effects of the new organisation on existing methods and procedure increasingly began to be felt. The LMS system of standard examinations of locomotives was expanded into new schedule BR No MP11, covering every type of locomotive in the country, as well as local variations in procedure caused by the quality of boiler feed water or the kind of service on which the locomotives were employed. In all, 141 items were listed, including forty under the 'X' examination scheme devised by Colonel Harold Rudgard, the chief officer for motive power; this superseded the Planned Servicing system but was the same in principle.

It would be difficult to find a greater contrast than that which existed between the detailed and comprehensive instruction contained in MP11 and the brief examination schedule outlined in LNER CME circular 189, which reads:

'Periodical Examination of Engines and Tenders in Running Sheds
The periods of the Special Examination of various parts of Engines and Tenders have been revised etc. etc.

IF IN THE OPINION OF THE DISTRICT LOCOMOTIVE SUPERINTENDENT MORE FREQUENT EXAMINATION IS NECESSARY OF ANY PARTICULAR COMPONENT OF ANY TYPE OF LOCOMOTIVE ARRANGEMENTS SHOULD BE MADE ACCORDINGLY'

This followed by a schedule summarised below defining the *maximum* frequency at which the components listed were to be examined:

Monthly	wheels, tyres, tenders and tanks with water pick up.
6 Monthly	Westinghouse top head, tenders and tanks without water pick up.
10,000 Miles	injectors, brakes of all types, axlepads, trimmings.
20,000 Miles	valves*, pistons, big-ends, coupling rods, crank pins, bogies, lubricators, mechanical and sight feed.

* Slide valves ⅝in thick and less, every 5,000 miles.

The examination of boilers, safety valves, water and pressure gauges came under a separate schedule. Much could be read into that qualification 'Maximum frequency of examination' which in former days was freely exercised to cut working expenses to a minimum. Nevertheless, it was not accepted as a valid excuse for a failure caused by running a locomotive beyond the scheduled period – distinctly a 'heads I win, tails you lose' situation. During the slump the same principle was applied by the LNER to cleaning locomotives, which according to class were not permitted to be cleaned more often than once daily for express passenger types, twice a week for other passenger and suburban tank engines, weekly for freight and only once a month for shunting engines.

The scheduled time allowance for cleaning an N7 class 0–6–2T was nine hours made up as follows: motion three hours, wheels two hours, boiler, tanks and bunker three hours, and inside the cab, one hour. The last generally was omitted as the firemen of a regularly manned engine would keep the cab and boiler front clean, thus permitting the rest to be cleaned right through in an eight-hour shift by one man, although the compulsory meal break of twenty minutes to be taken between the third and fifth hour on duty did create problems. There were also arguments at times about whether a locomotive was sufficiently dirty to qualify for the 25% additional time allowance for an exceptionally dirty machine, usually interpreted as one requiring the use of a scraper to peel off dirt that had accumulated on wheel spokes, brake gear and similar places.

NE16/136   17 June 1957

District Motive Power Superintendent,
Norwich.

Coupled Axleboxes: Manganese Liner (B1)

Since my report of 29.1.51. (your ref G/E/91), the advent of the Britannia class 4–6–2 has displaced the B1 class locomotives from the best express work, consequently there has been a noticeable reduction in the amount of axlebox maintenance required.

Nevertheless it is still necessary to overhaul driving and trailing coupled axleboxes of the B1 engines at 45, – 50,000 miles if these are to be kept in a fit condition for passenger work.

During 1956 the following coupled axleboxes were overhauled for knock in the horns or whitemetal exuding from the bearing

NORWICH

Engine No	Period under repair	Axleboxes
61042	31st May–28th June	Driving and trailing.
61043	12th July–3rd August	All coupled.
61045	3rd Sep. – 20th September	Driving and trailing.
61046	1st Mar. – 6th April	Driving.
61048	14th May – 7th June	All coupled.
61050	9th April – 4th May	Driving and trailing.
61270	17th July	Trailing boxes.
61232 (Stratford)	5th May – 5th June	Driving and trailing.
61234 (Stratford)	12th Sep. – 22nd Oct.	Trailing.
61235 (Stratford)	21st Oct. – 26th Nov.	Driving.

In addition the following bearings were re-fitted on account of heating.

Engine No	Date	Bearing
61249	3rd May	R.L.
61249	20th May	R.L.
61045	8th May	R.D.
61333	9th July	R.D.
61378	24th July	L.D.
61160	25th July	L.D.
61317	31st August	R.L.
61361	17th September	L.D.
61312	1st October	L.D.
61235	18th October	L.D.
61104	24th November	L.D.

Subjoined is tabulated the Axlebox horn clearances for the three B1s listed by you together with these from No 61223 just turned out of Stratford Works, as a measure of comparison.

B1 Class; Axlebox – Horn Clearance

Engine No	Approx. Mileages	Leading		Driving		Trailing	
		L	R	L	R	L	R
61223	(New)	.006	.006	.010	.002	.004	.010
61312	35,000	.008	.004	.014	.006	.003	.021
61270	40,000	.008	.006	.021	.012	.075	.065
61043	60,000	.006	.015	.051	.065	.075	.075

Statement of axleboxes and hornblocks of B1 class engines reconditioned for knock at Norwich since new in 1946–47 until 31 December 1950

Engine No	Mileage at which axleboxes were reconditioned	Out of service From	Out of service To	Repairs effected	Axlebox reconditioned = X · Axlebox renewed = R · Amount horns out of parallel = .00 inches	LL	RL	LD	RD	LT	RD	Man hours Skilled	Man hours Unskilled	Ultimate mileage when shopped
1047	69,798	6.9.47	24.10.47	Driving and trailing boxes rebored and refitted to horns	Boxes			X	X	X	X	65	76	89,306
	51,464	3.11.49	12.12.49	Driving boxes refitted, trailing boxes reconditioned. Horns refaced	Boxes			X	X	X	X	128	81	
					Horns			3/64	3/64	3/64	1/32			
	73,084	17.4.50	11.5.50	Leading and driving boxes renewed. Trailing boxes reconditioned All horns refaced and journals turned	Boxes	R	R	R	R	X	X	275	129	78,238
					Horns									
1049	56,171	12.8.47	25.8.47	Driving and trailing boxes refitted				X	X	X	X	65	76	90.083
	45,821	19.3.49	8.4.49	*To Stratford Works* for all coupled boxes renewing and horns re-facing		R	R	R	R			?	38	
	71,961	8.9.49	28.9.49	Both trailing boxes refitted	Boxes / Boxes			X	X	X	X	34	38	103,463
1050	36,358	19.11.48	29.12.48	Leading and driving boxes renewed Trailing boxes reconditioned All horns refaced	Boxes	.004	.030	.003	.003	.004	.003	246	125	85,895
					Horns	.008	.006	.007	.004	.043	.041			
	68,344	18.8.49	2.9.49	Both driving boxes refitted	Boxes			X	X			31	38	
	36,415	25.11.50	12.12.50	Both driving boxes renewed. LD hot. RD broken	Boxes			R	R			41	43	Still at work

B1 Class engines

Average time and cost of renovating coupled axleboxes and horncheeks
at Norwich
(Based on repairs to engines Nos 1050 and 1051 in 1948/49)

Nature of Repair	Leading or driving (bronze)		Trailing (cast steel)	
	Man Hours		*Man Hours*	
	Skilled	*Unskilled*	*Skilled*	*Unskilled*
Wheel Drop				
1. Removing and replacing any one pair of coupled wheels	15	30	15	30
Hornblocks				
2. Refacing any one pair	24	–	24	–
Axleboxes, remetalled only				
3. Remetalling (one pair)	3	–	6	–
			8 if boss liners refastened	
4. Boring and facing (one pair)	5	–	5	–
5. Bedding on journal (one pair)	8	8	8	8
Axleboxes renewing and new liners fixing				
6. Removing worn horncheek and wheel boss liners and attaching new liners (one pair)	–	–	45	5
7. Making and fixing copper rivets for hornliners	–	–		
8. Trying up and marking-off for boring	5	5		
9. Turning 16 brass countersink set screws	–	–	4	–
10. Planing for horns (one pair)	8	–	20	–
11. Boring and facing (one pair)	5	–	5	–
12. Bedding on journals (one pair)	8	8	8	8
13. Journals turning (one axle)	8	–	8	–

Wages Cost	*Skilled*	*Unskilled*	*Skilled*	*Unskilled*
(a) Reconditioning one pair of axleboxes.	31 plus 38 = £9.12.6.		34 plus 38 = £10.4.6.	
(b) Renewing or re-linering one pair including refacing horns and journals turning.	73 plus 43 = £16.17.4.		129 plus 43 = £25.9.2.	

CHAPTER 12

RELIEF DUTIES

During Mr L. P. Parker's regime as motive power superintendent I spent long periods away from Norwich relieving at other depots, and in 1949–1950 I was at my home station for less than six months. The first half of 1949 was spent at Stratford which I found much changed from the bustling, confident depot that I knew before the war. Like all London depots it was much slower in recovering from the effects of wartime shortage of men and materials than those in the country. This was due a lot to the difficulty in recruiting and keeping men of any calibre to fill vacancies, on account of the railways' inability to compete with the higher wages paid in outside industry such as Ford at Dagenham. Late starts due to a shortage of lamps or firing tools, the lack of which could sometimes be remedied by a search of ships' chandler stores in London's dockland, were commonplace – so too were those caused by a shortage of steam or a last-minute failure of a locomotive, which blocked in those behind. For example, on 8 April 1949 five locomotives were left by the steam raiser with their fires nearly out and insufficient water in their boilers, while a further five were each delayed ten minutes apiece in raising steam. On the previous day no repairs received attention between 11.50am and 12.30pm because the fitters were holding an 'indignation meeting' in the machine shop over the dismissal by the contractor of the canteen manager. Stoppages of this kind, usually the result of disputes as to who did what, and fomented by a communist shop steward were of frequent occurrence. There was also trouble with the ashpits, due to lack of maintenance through the war years.

Despite all these difficulties it is to Stratford's credit that it had succeeded in halving the number of locomotives stopped daily compared with January 1946, when out of its allocation of 365 an average of 45 tender and the same number of tank engines were out of service each day. In conditions such as these it was no sinecure to be responsible for operating what I believe was then still the most intensive steam suburban service in the world. I shall ever recall with admiration how on days when the stop list resembled in its length a Tibetan prayer flag, T. C. B. Miller, imperturbable as always, on entering my office would enquire with his usual dry humour – 'What is it this morning, ordered chaos or just chaos?' and then proceed to give sound advice on the best and quickest way of bringing the situation under control.

Fortunately for the preservation of our sanity, life at Stratford was not all gloom and doom. There were other and much more congenial subjects to occupy our minds, notably the arrival of Bulleid light Pacific No 34059 *Sir Archibald Sinclair* on loan from the Southern Region for trial purposes.

A most interesting and instructive day was spent at Nine Elms learning something of the mysteries of No 34059's construction from J. Pelham Maitland, an old LBSCR man, who did more than anyone else in nursing these unconventional machines through their early teething troubles and selling them to the Southern's travelling public. Particularly impressive was the extent to which electric welding was used in the repair of their steel fireboxes and the skill of the boilersmiths in welding in new diaphragm plates at the connection between the tubeplate and the Nicholson thermic syphons which were fitted with stays of monel metal pierced with a tell-tale hole to give warning of fracture. The importance of adhering closely to the correct method of cooling down this all-steel boiler and its subsequent washing-out every 4,000 miles was emphasised, also the importance of blowing-down daily to remove sludge – likewise correct water treatment by means of chemical briquettes. On the mechanical side, the neat and ingenious arrangement of the chain-driven valve gear was admirable but less so the crank case enclosing it. This held 48 gallons of oil and was prone to leak owing to the almost insuperable difficulty of devising a really satisfactory oil seal to accommodate the combined rise and fall and see-saw action of the crank axle.

On No 34059's arrival at Stratford I was entrusted with the interesting job of fitting it with a Hasler speed recorder. This instrument had been designed for an 80in wheel and in order to make it suitable for one of 74in diameter, an intermediate gearbox was designed and made at Norwich with the help of the Road Motor Department, which supplied the requisite gear wheels. The hill climbing ability of No 34059 when ascending Brentwood bank and the abundance of steam generated by the boiler was most impressive – less so the temperamental steam reverser, which was liable to fly into back gear if not very carefully controlled. In consequence, the Eastern Region driver pulled it up only as far as he dared, throttling the steam at the regulator, resulting in the ridiculous situation that out of the 280 lb/sq in produced by the boiler only 80 lb/sq in was being utilised in the cylinders.

On 17 May 1959 No 34059 worked a thirteen-coach special including the motive power superintendent's saloon to Norwich. On the return journey when nearing Tivetshall (15 miles) the steam pipe to the reverser fractured, causing the locomotive to run in full gear for the rest of the journey. A pressure of 80 lb/sq in to 90 lb/sq in was maintained in the steamchest and a speed of 50mph to 60mph (maximum 68mph). 3,200 gallons of water were used on the journey to Ipswich where a full tank (4,500 gallons) of water was taken. 1,228 gallons of this remained on arrival at Stratford, giving a total consumption of 6,472 gallons for a journey of just over 110 miles, more than double the normal consumption.

I resumed duty at Norwich at the end of July 1949 and was just beginning to pick up the dropped threads when I received urgent instructions to proceed immediately to Neasden, where during its shedmaster's absence on holiday a crisis had suddenly arisen. The power position at Neasden, always precarious as I well knew, had been steadily deteriorating for a long time due to an acute shortage of maintenance staff whose effective strength after taking into account those on holiday was only eleven fitters out of an establishment of twenty-two.

The inevitable result was that there was hardly a locomotive that could at all be relied upon. Two had failed in quick succession during the previous evening's peak hour service from Marylebone, causing two trains to be cancelled. These of all trains had to be the 5.42pm High Wycombe and the 6.10pm Wotton trains, used respectively by Barrington Ward and H. C. Johnson, the operating superintendent, for their homeward journeys. The telephone bells now began to ring to some purpose, resulting in the immediate transfer from Willesden of three Fowler 2–6–4 tanks and the loan of eight fitters who had volunteered to work temporarily at Neasden – three from Sheffield, two from Colwick (Nottingham) and one each from Crewe, Kentish Town and Stratford. Scapegoats for Headquarter's failure to recognise earlier a rapidly worsening power position were found in the persons of the shedmaster and district motive power superintendent who were relieved of their office. The latter, nearing retirement, tendered his resignation rather than submit to the humiliation of a special duties posting.

The memory of these unhappy events and the causes leading up to them left two deep and lasting impressions on my mind. Firstly of how vitally important it is for an engineer to repair the machinery for which he is responsible, at least as fast as the rate at which it wears out – in other words to apply the Macawbian principle to engineering. Secondly, if, as in the present instance this is impossible of attainment, then it is his duty (as my colonial experience had taught me) to give his senior officers early and adequate warning of the gravity of the situation in writing, and equally important for his own protection to keep a copy of that warning. This is the course that I adopted throughout the eight long months I spent at Neasden, the roughest and most demanding of my whole career.

Naturally, some changes had taken place at Neasden since the end of the war. New faces of many nationalities and races had replaced those of the Italian prisoners of war. The most noticeable change was in the steadily diminishing number of Coronation (A5) tank engines, for 38 years the mainstay of Marylebone's suburban service, as these were replaced by brand-new L1 class 2–6–4 tanks of Edward Thompson's design.

One aspect that remained unchanged was a chronic shortage of power – indeed, it had been made worse instead of better by the arrival of the new locomotives. The reasons for this deterioration was not far to seek. The first and most important was that there were far too many locomotives for a depleted fitting staff to maintain. Originally there had been 29 Coronation tanks to work 27 diagrams – now the allocation of A5s and L1s combined numbered 43, yet it was still necessary at times to borrow from King's Cross one and sometimes two N2 tanks in order to maintain the service, which meant keeping the signalboxes open during the night on the connecting line from Harringay. Complete cancellation of a night's boiler washing programme was also a commonplace. The only 'surplus' locomotives were those under or awaiting repair, which could not be removed from Neasden.

It was imperative to concentrate every effort on maintaining in serviceable condition those locomotives still running. This was of paramount importance, and there was no choice in the matter. It was also the case that these new tank engines, which it was confidently expected would put an end to Neasden's power problems, were proving to be a grave disappointment, giving as much and more trouble to maintain than the 38-year-old locomotives that they were replacing. In designing a powerful general-purpose locomotive of the 'go anywhere, do anything' description, a wide route availability is only attainable by cutting down the weight of metal in its construction, often at the expense of inadequate bearing surfaces. Earlier mention has been made of this in connection with the B1 4–6–0s; in the case of the L1 tank this was exaggerated by the smallness of its coupled wheels, 5ft 2in, for the high average speeds demanded by the Great Central's semi main line suburban services. Early complaints from drivers that their new locomotives were knocking themselves to pieces were but statements of fact. Detached wheel boss liners, the loss of which enabled a finger to be inserted between wheel boss and axlebox were commonplace; likewise horncheek liners shaken loose by impact and vibration were found resting on hornstays, and incredible though it may seem, one locomotive that I was called upon to inspect had lost a coupled axlebox crown bearing, not altogether surprising in view of the pounding these received, causing the white metal lining in the crown to loosen and exude sideways from the bearing. This excessive vibration caused the all-welded water tanks to split along their length at footplate level, also where they were arched to clear

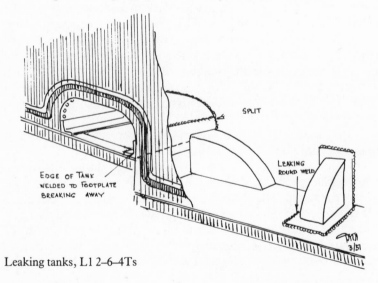

SPLIT

LEAKING ROUND WELD

EDGE OF TANK WELDED TO FOOTPLATE BREAKING AWAY

Leaking tanks, L1 2–6–4Ts

the expansion link and at the back of the coal bunker; water dripping from these bunker fractures onto the live electric rail made uncoupling on the Metropolitan line especially hazardous. W. G. Thorley, chief mechanical inspector, produced a comprehensive report dated 11 May 1950 and addressed to Col H. Rudgard, Chief Officer for Motive Power, the Railway Executive. An extract is given here:

Mechanical Items.
Certain features of the working at Neasden described above lead to a consideration of some of the factors which are responsible for the "uneasy" power position, and paramount among these factors appears to be the heavy incidence of running repairs among the L1 2–6–4 tank locomotives, of which 35 are now allocated to this depot, many of them new engines.

The principal difficulty in maintaining these locomotives in good mechanical condition arises from the poor performance of the coupled axleboxes, which is the worst for a recent design seen on any Region. An idea of the rapid deterioration suffered by these axleboxes after General Repair or from new engine is conveyed by the following data, representing the position at Neasden on 29 April 1950.

Engine No	*Coupled axlebox defects*	*Approximate miles since general repair, or new engine*
67707	L. trailing steel oil pipe broken off; metal loose in pockets of L.T. (L.D. ran hot 30.4.50).	23,000
67718	Both leading steel oil pipes broken. No metal in side pockets, and very little in top pocket of L. driving. L. trailing steel oil pipe broken off.	75,000 (accepted for shop repairs 22/3, still in service)
67720	No metal in side pockets of L.D., metal very loose in pockets of L.D. and L.L.	70,000
67751	L.L. steel oil pipe broken off. Metal loose in pockets of L.D. and R.T.	60,000
67758	L.T. steel oil pipe broken off; axlebox lubricator driving mechanism in very bad order.	50,000
67767	Metal missing from back side pocket of L.D.; metal loose in pockets of R.D.	30,000
67761	R.T. steel oil pipe broken. Metal falling out of all pockets of R.D.; lubricator driving gear in very bad order.	47,000

67769   No white metal in side pockets of L.D.   22,000
67773   Metal very loose in side pockets of L.D.;
            metal working out of top pocket of R.D.   20,000

On the same day that the above position was investigated, three other L1 engines were at King's Cross for attention to coupled axleboxes, and a fourth in service ran hot.

A footplate trip on No 67707 (see above) revealed that with fully opened regulator and 15% cut-off, the knock throughout the axleboxes and motion was very pronounced. A further trip on L1 7720, with similar conditions of regulator and cut-off produced a deafening knock and reversion had to be made quickly to ¼–½ regulator opening and 25% cut-off, which appears to be the usual combination adopted by enginemen in working these engines on the Marylebone suburban services.

It is apparent that eight of the nine engines listed above with axlebox defects will require the appropriate axleboxes removing for repairs as early as possible. The most common defects affecting coupled axleboxes and associated equipment are shown below:-
1. Loosening and eventual loss of white metal from bronze bearing shell.
2. Loosening of bearing shell in steel axlebox, resulting in shearing of set screws.
3. Breakage of steel oil pipe which is welded to steel axlebox; a fairly effective temporary repair can be made in the case of leading and driving axleboxes, but not on the trailing, in consequence of which the underkeep has to be removed at two-day intervals to enable it to be filled and so keep the axlebox lubricated. It is understood that a modified arrangement of oil pipes to the trailing coupled axleboxes has been authorised, but is not being applied to all engines, either when lifted at King's Cross or at repairs in the M.E. Shops.
4. Rapid wear of driving gear to mechanical lubricator; this may be due to the inertia effect of the main driving rod which weighs some 17 lbs., and to the inadequate bearing surface of the unlubricated joint pins, when working in conjunction with 5' 2" driving wheels at speeds of 60m.p.h.
   It is very often known that this driving gear is in need of overhaul, but the repair has to be deferred because in many cases it involves the removal of the expansion link of the valve gear.

Crossheads.
The rate of crosshead liner wear is also high, involving remetalling of crossheads at from 10–15,000 miles. It is stated that the rate of wear is much higher on engines not fitted with dust shields over the leading coupled wheels, which when fitted appear to prevent brake block abrasions from reaching the slide bars.

Many changes in personnel had taken place since 1945, Ted Claxton had retired from the post of leading fitter, to be succeeded by a man past middle age who had spent all of his previous career in Stratford works and who had no running shed experience whatsoever. The reason for appointing to such a key position a man lacking such an essential qualification must remain a matter for surmise – most probably because he was the only applicant, for in the post-war years men were becoming increasingly reluctant to move homes in order to achieve promotion, not only on account of an acute shortage of houses in urban areas but also the great disparity in house prices as between town and country. The new incumbent, although he strove manfully to overcome his lack of essential running shed experience, could not be expected to learn quickly the art of knowing how to keep ailing locomotives running. Needless to say it was the old faithfuls, the ever-dwindling nucleus of Great Central fitters, who bore the brunt of maintenance, and the credit for keeping Neasden going in these difficult times was entirely theirs.

The position on the boiler side was even more critical, for out of the original five railway boilermakers only Bill House, then nearing 70 years of age, remained. Only he could be entrusted with the important task of examining locomotive fireboxes and signing the certificate of their fitness for service. Filling the other four vacancies were two Maltese boilermakers from HM naval dockyard in Valetta, and two from Clyde shipyards whose experience appeared to be confined to plating work; one demanded 'height money' for going up and doing some work on the coaling plant, displaying at its top a huge red flag like the one to be seen flying above the coaling plant at the neighbouring Willesden MPD, because he alleged it to be unsafe. Whether politically inspired or not, it was not taken too seriously and soon removed.

The artisans' mates or labourers as they were termed under the district rates agreement governing the Great Central's workshop staff were a veritable league of nations; there were Irishmen from north and south of the border, a Greek, an Armenian, an Indian driver off the Bengal Nagpur Railway, a fitter from the Bombay & Central India line, a Calcutta jew, several West Indians and West Africans, and for a short while a pupil from the Chinese National Railways.

Among the shed conciliation grades there was a strong

contingent of Poles from the Polish Resettlement Corps, excellent fellows who did boiler-washing, steam raising, tube cleaning and the like; two of the best steam-raisers were Maros and Janick, who could always be relied upon to raise steam in a locomotive rapidly when the necessity arose, as it often did. The record for raising steam was achieved on 14 February 1950 by Running Foreman Sid Wood, who in order to avoid cancellation of an evening peak hour train himself lit up at 3.30pm after a cold water washout L1 No 7751. By dint of feeding the fire with wood he had 80 lb/sq in showing on the gauge by 4.40pm – not at all good for the firebox, but fully justified in the circumstances.

Here I would like to pay tribute to the wonderfully loyal support that I received throughout these long difficult months not only from the three running foremen, Jack Elvey, Harold Floyd and Sid Wood but also the Neasden enginemen whom I had got to know from my daily footplate trips during the war, without whose support and encouragement my task would have been not only impossible of achievement but quite intolerable, and I remember them with gratitude.

A sense of the ridiculous was at times a great help, as for instance on that memorable occasion in the autumn of 1949 when both the Great Central routes to the north were blocked on the same day by the failure of two Neasden locomotives – that seemed at the time to be the ultimate in misfortune. The first failure occurred shortly before noon when an N7 tank working the Ruislip—Marylebone shuttle service dropped its motion at Wembley Hill, blocking the line to Princes Risborough. Hardly had this been cleared when news came that L1 No 7756 had dropped its right-hand slidebar at Great Missenden, completely blocking the Metropolitan joint line just as the afternoon peak service was building up. As if to make doubly sure that the line should be effectively blocked, fate decreed that the slidebar in falling should be struck by the rapidly rotating big-end, and being driven upwards pierce the side tank, so letting out all the water. Being on Metropolitan territory this failure was dealt with by that company's breakdown staff who in order to save valuable time were quite ruthless in their use of a cutting torch. I was called upon subsequently to account for this wanton mutilation of a practically new locomotive to an irate chief mechanical engineer, who demanded to know why it was considered necessary to burn off the lug on the crosshead connecting it to the union link when this could have been easily released by the removal of a pin.

A frequent visitor to Neasden at this time was a senior officer from Western Region control centre at High Wycombe who came to find out for himself the causes of these frequent disruptions to its Birmingham service. During one of these visits I was summoned to an N7 tank that had failed with a defective hand brake when about to leave the shed. The cause proved to be an accumulation of coaldust packed solid in the hand brake column; this I cleaned out myself rather than cause a delay by explaining to some one else what needed doing. The look of astonishment on Mr Galley's face when I returned to the office to wash my hands is not likely to be forgotten nor his remark 'Had I not seen it for myself, I would not have believed such things possible!'

Earlier, a little light relief had been afforded by a test made in Neasden works to see if a Westinghouse-braked L1 could pump sufficient air to operate not only the train brakes but also the air-operated doors of the London Transport new Metadyne stock. If successful this would have enabled it to be hauled right though to Aylesbury over the non-electrified section, thus dispensing with the need to retain compartment stock specially for steam haulage north of Rickmansworth and its own electric locomotives for haulage south. This test proved to be a complete fiasco as might have been foreseen, for having opened the doors it then took about ten minutes to pump up enough air to close them, leaving none to release the brakes. Even if this experiment had proved successful a separate reservoir independent of that used for braking purposes, similar to that on GER locomotives for their air-operated water scoop power reverser, and sanding would have been necessary.

There was for a time a welcome improvement in the power position as a result of the help given by the eight volunteers but this was short-lived, as these men could not be expected to stay indefinitely at Neasden. All had returned to their home depots by November at which time the repair position had become as bad as ever, as may be judged from the following detailed statement produced at a conference I attended at Neasden on 21 November 1949. This was presided over by E. H. Ker, locomotive engineer, and attended by J. A. Frampton, district locomotive superintendent. It was decided to withdraw permanently from Neasden six L1s currently under repair and to despatch to King's Cross for attention all locomotives standing at Neasden either partly dismantled or awaiting repair, as soon as they could be made moveable. This bold and momentous decision was to prove the turning point in Neasden's fortunes, for relieved of the burden of maintaining unwanted locomotives attention could now be devoted to those in service. Meanwhile the position was further improved by the return of newly-repaired locomotives from Gorton Works and the departure thence of a few of the old crocks fit only for shunting the neighbouring wagon shops or Marylebone coal yard. Another result of that meeting which gave Neasden a much-needed new look was the weekly visit of Dick Ball and his gang of Polish engine cleaners from King's Cross.

Concurrent with this brighter outlook was the arrival at Neasden at the request of the GWR enginemen at Aylesbury, a small shed shared jointly by the GWR and GCR, of two of its big 2–6–2 tanks, Nos 6129 and 6166, which proved to be excellent locomotives. An interesting day was spent at Old Oak Common learning what and what not to do in the way of maintaining GWR design locomotives, for instance that the position of the top and bottom elements units of the Swindon superheater were on no account to be exchanged because the element tubes were arranged in the shape of a horseshoe, and if inverted would retain and become clogged with ash.

NEASDEN, M.P.D.
Power Position on 21 November 1949

Number of Engines required to cover Suburban Passenger Diagrams			29
	A5	L1	
Number of Engines allocated	*21*	*23*	
In and Awaiting Works	6	4	
Under Depot Repair or Waiting Material	4	5	
Available for Traffic	*11*	*14*	25
a) in Good condition	5	2	
b) in Indifferent condition	6	8	
c) in Poor condition	–	4	
Available for Washing-out and Examination			Nil
Shortfall made good with unsuitable types of Engines from cancelled goods trains			

I was also initiated into the mysteries of the retaining valve and crosshead-driven vacuum pump which could bring the locomotive to a grinding halt after a few revolutions of the wheels unless the ejector which made a decidedly vulgar rasping noise were not opened first. This was just the opposite of what happened when a locomotive equipped with a Dreadnought type ejector and vacuum brake cylinders was made to function as a simple vacuum brake merely by placing the banjo handle in the fully applied position and when desiring to stop, opening the small ejector – experimentally interesting but of little or no practical value.

I knew that hidden under layers of paint on these GWR locomotives were those twin adornments that characterised most Great Western types – a copper cap to the chimney and a brass casing to the safety valves. The paint was scraped off carefully and with the aid of scour patches and much elbow grease these components were made to shine like the proverbial fireman's helmet of old.

Nos 6129 and 6166 were allocated to the Princes Risborough service, on which they did exceedingly well, considering that their tanks held no more than 2,000 gallons of water compared with the 2,280 gallons on the A5s, with their duplex water scoop. The power position had now improved sufficiently to permit an occasional day out. A favourite excursion was the 11.00am from Marylebone to Princes Risborough on either of the 2–6–2Ts, then across the Kimble branch on an N5 to Aylesbury for a pub lunch, returning on the Metropolitan line as far as Rickmansworth on either an A5 or an L1 tank which the Metropolitan men put through its paces, often running the seven-minute sections in four-and-a-half minutes. On several occasions I boarded the electric locomotive that took over at Rickmansworth, and on the first trip was somewhat startled by a series of loud reports coming from the motor compartment caused, I was told, by the pneumatically-operated contractors effecting the various stages of field weakening. Changing trains at Finchley Road I was back at Neasden in good time to sign the day's output of letters – altogether a most enjoyable outing.

The condition of Neasden locomotives had now improved sufficiently for Mr Parker to deem that the time was ripe for instituting on a grand scale one of his three-day 'blitzes' on local passenger train punctuality, whereby each locomotive crew was accompanied by a locomotive inspector (some coming from as far afield as Peterborough) who kept strict account of any time lost or made up and the reason. These blitzes frequently took the operating people by surprise, but after the first day they too began to smarten their working; distant signals never previously known to be off were lowered during these three days and habitual latecomers at stations were disconcerted to see their trains which usually waited for them leave at their booked times. The results when tabled came as revelation to all concerned; the total time lost by locomotives during each day's working amounted to something like 40 minutes; the time *regained* by locomotives on account of signal checks and detention at stations was over 380 minutes or nearly ten times the amount they had lost!

This welcome improvement in Neasden's performance is reflected by the percentage of its surburban trains arriving at their destinations on time during business hours. Statements issued by the Railway Executive Committee on alternate months show the performance of the top three of 24 of its principal suburban services to and from London arranged in order of punctuality.

Fred Clements, later chief mechanical and electrical engineer, LMR was appointed shedmaster Neasden in May 1950, and my task accomplished I returned to Norwich. Neasden Loco has long since been demolished and the memory of these spells of relief duty during and after the war seem now like a recurring bad dream.

Back at Norwich I found everything in excellent shape. John Brown, an ex-Cambridge apprentice promoted to the rank of major for his wartime exploits in restoring to working order locomotives sabotaged by the Germans during the retreat through Italy, was now mechanical foreman and had been acting as locomotuve shed master during my long absence. John Brown, destined to become a senior railway inspector with the Department of Transport, was succeeded by another first-rate man in John Bramwell.

Heated bearings continued to be a problem at all depots and no further improvement in locomotive availability could be expected until their number had been drastically reduced.

The classes of engines most subject to hot boxes were those with inadequate bearing surfaces and a high piston loading, where any inadequacy in lubrication was bound to result in heating. Mr Parker tackled this problem by the introduction at all the principal depots of a special lubrication squad consisting of a fitter ('Put your best fitter on it, Harvey') and two mates, whose job it was regularly and thoroughly to overhaul the lubrication system of every locomotive as it came in for its shed day. Special tools were provided, a miniature pair of tongs, small enough to pass between wheel spokes for the extraction and subsequent re-insertion after cleaning of trimmings (renewed at three-monthly intervals) in axlebox oil wells. Syringes were provided for extracting of water from oil cups, oil wells and axlebox keeps – at the larger depots vacuum-operated extractors performed this operation more speedily. While the two mates responsible for making and keeping up a stock of trimmings were thus engaged, the fitter was busy searching for leaking and broken oil pipes, checking and adjusting mechanical lubricators, cleaning out and renewing ball valves and seatings as necessary in anti-carbonisers or atomisers.

In order to ensure that locomotives were properly lubricated by crews, a HQ lubrication inspector was appointed to visit depots and make spot checks of locomotive preparation. The result of these measures was a dramatic reduction in the number of heated bearings.

For many years footplate and artisan staff alike had complained quite justifiably that they were told little or nothing about the purpose or functioning of the special equipment that appeared on locomotives from time to time, or about new repair techniques. A serious attempt to overcome this lack of communication was the regular appearance in the notice cases of two bulletins, the *Craftsman's News Letter* and *ESMIG, The Eastern Section Mutual Improvement Class Guide*.

Another excellent innovation that enabled one to see at a glance if the April and October inspection of the sealed canisters, containing twelve up-to-date detonators and two red flags carried by every GE section locomotive had been carried out, was shown by their colour, sky blue for summer skies and white for winter.

The summer of 1950 passed pleasantly enough with an autumn holiday spent in France. This break was followed by spells of relief duties at King's Cross and Bradford respectively. Difficulty in recruiting staff in London had become so acute ('You will get no one until you increase your wages and lower your medical standard' said the manager of St Pancras Labour Exchange) that King's Cross was no longer able to maintain without help its fleet of streamlined A4 class 4-6-2s. These were sent to Grantham, then an important depot half-way between London and York, for their heavier mileage examination, where an excellent job was made of them. The situation in Bradford was in complete contrast to that in London – there was no shortage of skilled men eager to undertake additional work, especially among the footplate staff. Motive power at Bradford consisted mainly of J50 class 0–6–0 tank engines (Ardsley tanks) for freight transfer duties and ex-London suburban 0–6–2 tank engines from which the condensing gear had been removed for the passenger service between Bradford and Leeds. The sight, sound and fury of these saturated, slide-valve N1 class locomotives belting up the 1 in 50 gradient to Laisterdyke, especially at night when they gave magnificent pyrotechic displays, is something to remember! Another memory is of a trip to Keighley on a Great Central C13 class 4–4–2 tank during a period of hard frost, and of the crackling noise made as the locomotive snapped off yard-long icicles hanging from the roofs of the very wet tunnels near Denholme. A visit to Bradford's City Road goods warehouse, where huge bales of Australian wool were stored, revealed a fine example of Victorian engineering in the shape of a pair of compound hydraulic pumping engines by Tannett Walker fitted with Meyer double expansion gear.

One dull drizzly day in January 1951 I went to see R. L. Vereker, formerly in charge of the Crimpsall shops at Doncaster and then locomotive superintendent of the Leeds District of the former GNR, in his headquarters at Ardsley, the principal freight depot. A smell of burning pervaded the atmosphere; this came from a subterranean fire which for years had been smouldering in the coal measures below the depot! A massive bund wall of concrete had been built round the foundations of the mechanical coaling plant in order to prevent their disintegration by heat, the degree of which was measured daily by lowering thermometers into a number of 2in steel tubes sunk into the ground at intervals round the plant. Wisps of steam came from these tubes and from cracks in the surrounding earth burnt red by the heat, which during wet weather increased when fed by the oxygen in the water percolating through the soil. On such a dismal afternoon it seemed indeed desolate and made me more than ever thankful to have made my home amid the green fields of East Anglia. Whether Mr Vereker, then nearing retirement, shared these sentiments is doubtful, but shortly afterwards he came to Norwich to fill the vacancy created by C. N. Morris's promotion. Many men during the last year or so of their career tended to delegate more and more of their work to subordinates on whom they increasingly relied to keep things running smoothly. Not so Rupert Vereker – he was into everything, a veritable human dynamo of energy, right up to the day of his retirement four years later.

His arrival at Norwich coincided with the appointment of a bricklayer to the establishment (I had asked for a second blacksmith!) for whom at first it was difficult to find employment that did not encroach on the work of the civil engineer's department. Like most new brooms Mr Vereker was intent on making sweeping alterations, not only to the organisation which was to be remodelled on Great Northern lines, but to the antiquated and inconvenient layout of the general and staff offices, between which there was no internal connection. Our newly engaged bricky was soon busy making doorways where none had been before and blocking up one of the numerous transverse passages separating the several offices. These alterations were greatly appreciated by the clerical staff, especially the typists, during the winter months.

A plan long deferred to modernise the oil stores was revived, and on receiving RLV's warm approval was soon being prosecuted with energy and enthusiasm. Improved handling and dispensing arrangements were installed and these by eliminating the former chronic waste of oil, demurrage charges on oil drums, and the need to employ an additional storesman, effected an annual saving in oil alone of £1,000 – a lot of money in those days. All this was achieved by our own staff using stock material (2in vacuum pipe, Westinghouse cocks, etc.) and redundant equipment, the only new items purchased were two immersion heaters for warming cylinder oil. The oil store, conveniently situated at the corner of the shed adjoins the tank house and is part of the original 1843 structure; it is 40ft long and 25ft wide. Prior to alteration eight large cubical oil tanks mounted on low piers took up approximately a third of this limited space at one end, leaving the remainder for the accommodation of engine head lamps, oil bottles, buckets of tools, firing shovels and coal picks; at weekends when the minimum number of locomotives was at work, up to 80 sets of equipment had to be stored. Drums of oil for replenishing the storage tanks were rolled into the stores from a barrel park in the yard about 30yd away, being lifted by chain blocks suspended from an overhead monorail. Although occupying a lot of space the tanks, containing the several grades of lubricating oil, were of insufficient capacity and had to be frequently replenished, this situation was further aggravated by the length of time it took to dispense oil due to the inadequate size of the taps which were often allowed to run unattended while the storeman left the store to roll in a fresh barrel of oil. As a result the scale of oil allowances was ignored, oil bottles were filled to capacity regardless of mileage, often overflowing on to the floor. During winter months mud and ice adhering to the oil drums melting in the warmth of the stores, found its way into the storage tanks.

The position on the tool issuing side was just as bad. An insufficiency of storage racks and those there were badly sited resulted in the extremely limited floor space becoming cluttered with buckets of tools, head lamps, oil bottles and so on, making it difficult to find the right bucket and often resulting in equipment being given to the wrong man. Frequent altercations ensued and it was not unknown for enginemen to enter the stores and help themselves. Poor as the facilities were, better use could have been made of them had the three shifts of stores issuers, all light work men, taken a little more interest in their duties and co-operated better.

Certain jobs on the railway registered as light work posts were reserved for those members of the staff unfortunate enough to have been maimed or incapacitated in the course of their duties. These light work posts included such jobs as storemen, timekeepers, telephone attendants, messengers, ticket collectors, lavatory attendants, lookout men and the like and were open to all those thus disabled, regardless of their department. The railway honoured its obligation to employ up to 6% of its establishment of war disabled men. In addition employment had to be found for green card men registered with the Ministry of Labour who for health reasons could not carry out all the duties required from able-bodied men. Obviously some departments offered more scope than others for the employment of the disabled. Sometimes in a desire to find a place for such men, the selectors gave less consideration than they should have done to the candidates suitability for the duties expected of him, and this at Norwich had resulted in an unduly high proportion of square pegs in round holes.

Two vacancies for stores issuers occurring at that time were filled in the absence of any other candidates by two ex main line drivers removed from the footplate on account of colour-blindness. No better choice could have been made for as enginemen, understanding the needs of enginemen, they were respected by their colleagues. They took a great pride and interest in their new duties, keeping the stores clean and tidy, besides polishing the brass gauges and cocks until they shone as brightly as the boiler mountings on the locomotives that they had recently driven. The appointment of these two enginemen, coupled with improvements about to be described transformed the oil stores from being a place of which I was heartily ashamed into one that I could display with pride to visitors.

The first move was to increase the effective floor area of the stores by transferring the eight oil storage tanks into the adjacent tank house, used hitherto only for the storage of sponge cloths and lumber of various kinds. Additional space was given by raising the tanks aloft, which, by increasing the natural head, also improved the flow of oil from the tanks. Two 12in rolled-steel joists for supporting the tanks, surplus to requirements at Ipswich where a new motive power depot was being built, were lengthened as necessary by splicing on extensions and installed parallel to one another in the tank house about 12ft above ground level.

In order to provide much needed extra storage capacity for lubricating oil, two tall, flat tanks with a combined capacity of 2,300 gallons and surplus to requirements at Melton Constable were installed on the girder at the western end of the tank house. Due to their height it was decided that the most convenient way of getting them into the tank house would be to remove temporarily its multi-paned, cast-iron framed window and with a crane lift them straight out of the wagon, and passing them through the window opening, lower them on to the western girder, moving them into their final position on rollers. This operation was carried out successfully with the Ipswich 20-ton steam crane, borrowed specially for this operation because its short jib could be more easily manoeuvred through the window opening than that of the Norwich 35-ton Ransome crane; the chipped condition of several bricks in the window arch bear mute witness to the fact that it did so.

The next stage was to provide a quick and expeditious way of transferring the contents of the barrels to the storage tanks, if possible without removing them from the wagon in which they came, to avoid handling costs and later finding another wagon in which the empty drums could be returned. Closure of the Mid Suffolk Light Railway produced just what was needed, a small pumping installation driven by a single-cylinder Lister petrol engine, formerly used for pumping water into the tank at Laxfield. This was overhauled and a four-branch manifold made; each branch was fitted with a cock thus enabling whatever grade of oil being pumped to be directed into the appropriate storage tank. All that was needed now was a loading arm or crane with a hose long enough to reach to all corners of a wagon, thus enabling drums to be emptied where they stood and returned empty the same day, in the same wagon. A loading arm satisfying these requirements was made from a length of 2in vacuum pipe terminating at its upper end in a swan neck to which an equal length of boilerwashing hose was attached. This assembly, resembling in appearance a giant sized coachman's whip, was pivotted on trunnions at its lower end and being counterbalanced with two signal arm balance weights was free to swing easily up and down, thus enabling the suction hose to reach a drum anywhere in a wagon. The results more than fulfilled our expectations; 48 drums in two wagons were pumped dry regularly in an eight-hour shift and once 63 drums were emptied in a day. Constant attendance during pumping was not required – a visit at five-minute intervals to transfer the suction hose from one drum to the next was all that was necessary once the bungs had been removed. The stores issuers, relieved of the labour of rolling and hoisting heavy oil drums, were now free to attend to their prime duty of dispensing oil in the amounts prescribed in the scale of oil allowance, roughly one pint of cylinder and four pints of lubricating oil per 100 miles for locomotives and double this amount for the larger types.

Other means were adopted for handling cylinder oils since these were too thick and viscous when cold to respond to pumping. A pair of compressed-air charging vessels (Westinghouse brake main reservoirs) was installed outside the oil stores adjacent to the wagon road, into which the contents of the drums rolled from the wagon across a drawbridge, drained. When full the admission cock on the charging cylinder was closed, compressed air turned on and its contents blown into the storage tank above, an operation which took about an hour-and-a-half depending on the ambient temperature at the time. A treacle or chopper valve was used to dispense cylinder oil into pint and quart measures, the only oil for which these were now used.

Signal oil for headlamps was pumped direct from the suppliers' road tankers which were equipped with a pump for that purpose. Gauge lamp oil was transferred to its tank by a small Mumford boiler feed pump (ex Melton Constable) connected to the compressed air supply. Both grades of lamp oil were conveniently dispensed by push-button taps from discarded wash basins and modified to deliver a thin stream of oil into the lamp cistern. Head and gauge lamp cisterns were not interchangeable, being different both in size and shape. The design of the fixtures took this difference into account, thus ensuring that only the correct grade of oil went into a cistern, very important in the case of gauge lamps exposed to the heat of a boiler, which if filled with thin oil were liable to catch fire. A considerable saving in lamp oil resulted from transferring responsibility for trimming lamps from the firemen (to whom, following GE practice, a pint of lamp oil in a small bottle was issued) to the toolmen since a headlamp cistern held but one-eighth of a pint!

The tool stores next received attention. An old brick half partition wall was demolished and replaced by a column made from superheater flue. This alteration slightly increased the floor space and permitted the tool racks to be repositioned at right-angles to the serving hatch, which was lowered and widened in order to save the storemen unnecessary exertion in lifting heavy buckets of tools up and down. Additional tool racks were made, each allotted to a particular classes of locomotive and labelled accordingly. A slate at the end of each rack marked with its hook number was provided for the toolman to chalk the locomotive number to which the equipment belonged as he hung it up, so making it easy for the toolman to find the equipment.

The success achieved by these improved handling methods highlighted the need to examine other operations where labour was being used wastefully. Loading defective bearing springs into wagons for despatch to main works, by a gang of four to six cleaners, and their subsequent unloading on return, was a case in point.

During 1949 no fewer than 890 bearing springs were sent away for repair from Norwich, including those sent in from its sub-sheds, for a total allocation of 117 locomotives. The principal reason for this abnormally high number of weak and broken bearing springs was the enforced re-use during the wartime rationing of steel of too many old spring plates when rebuilding springs. An acute shortage of spring steel existed well into the early 1950s. It became so bad that for a period of seven consecutive days a daily exchange of B1 class seven-plate bogie springs took place between locomotives coming in for their shed days and those going out, in order to keep the fleet running until a replacement for the broken spring could be obtained.

A heavy 15-plate driving spring was as much as two fairly strong men could lift and the risk of injury to the young cleaners used for loading was considerable. It was therefore decided to construct a crane for this purpose, utilising a redundant wall crane formerly used for lifting wheels into the wheel lathe. Unfortunately the shed wall to which the crane might have been attached was too far from the wagon road for it to be of any use; instead the crane was attached to a strong box-girder column made by joining together with butt straps and rivets two channel section carriage solebars. This post was erected on a foundation of short lengths of rail concreted into the ground adjacent to the wagon road and stayed from the shed wall by two boiler longitudinal stays. Two young cleaners were now all that were needed to load and unload springs without difficulty or risk to themselves.

In the machine shop a crane was needed urgently to replace the chain blocks suspended from a wooden roof truss above the big lathe and used by the turner to lift on and off its heavy chucks and faceplates. A column similarly constructed to the one just described was therefore erected under the roof truss in question to assist in supporting the weight of the line shafting carried on it, beside relieving it of a load that it was not designed to bear; to this column a pair of cranes also made locally were attached to serve the machines below.

Mention has been made earlier of the help that Norwich was able to give less fortunate depots where great difficulty existed in recruiting staff, by engaging and training lads to fill their cleaning vacancies. The idea occurred to Tom Sands, district locomotive inspector that it would be an even greater help if these lads were passed for firing duties before they left Norwich.

To enable this to be done a mobile training school equipped with a model railway properly signalled for demonstrating operating rules was required, so enabling lads at small outstations to have equality of training with those at the district shed at Norwich. A suitable vehicle became available in the old Great

Central directors' saloon, which was equipped at Norwich with a model railway generously presented by Messrs Trix Ltd. Sectional models of locomotive equipment were prepared and installed – these are now on exhibition at the National Railway Museum and some are illustrated in *A Manual of Steam Locomotive Restoration and Preservation* (David & Charles, 1980). This coach gave excellent service in producing fully fledged firemen to the end of steam traction at Norwich in 1962 when it was broken-up and its contents dispersed, the model railway going to the Jenny Lind Home for Children.

It was my duty as shed master, as R. L. Vereker emphasised, to conduct LPP round the depot (It's all yours, Mister!) on his regular visits to Norwich. It was an education to listen to the verbal sparring that took place between these two redoubtable but quite dissimilar personalities. By using the somewhat tactless expression 'on the main line' when referring to GN practice, the little man laid himself wide open to a rapier thrust 'To which line to you refer, Vereker, the Cambridge or the Colchester main line?'

CHAPTER 13

THE BRITANNIAS

The year 1951 was notable for the introduction into regular service on the GE line of a Pacific type locomotive, the Britannia class, first of the new BR Standard range. These locomotives were an immediate success in East Anglia where they did most of their best work. I regard the decade 1951–1961 when the Britannias were at Norwich as the crowning years of my career.

In the Britannias, with their 20-ton axle load and a grate half as big again as those of the locomotives they displaced, GE enginemen now had at their disposal a reserve of power that enabled time to be kept on the fastest trains even with coal of indifferent quality. A comparison of the adhesion and total weight of the several types of six-coupled express engines employed on the GER system between 1912 and 1951 reflects the progress made in strengthening or replacing the many old and weak underline bridges on its main lines. The adhesion weight alone of the Britannias exceeded that permitted forty years earlier for the whole locomotive.

The timetable was recast to take advantage of the power of these new locomotives by the introduction of an hourly service of fast,

Year	Class	Grate area sq ft	Locomotive adhesive weight		Locomotive total weight		Tractive* effort lb
			tons	cwt	tons	cwt	
1912	1500	26.5	43	8	57	10	21,969
1932	B12/3	31.0	48	2	69	10	21,969
1928	B17	27.5	54	6	77	5	25,380 @ 200 lb/sq in 22,900 @ 180 lb/sq in
1946	B1	27.9	52	10	71	3	26,878
1951	7MT	42.0	60	15	94	0	32,150

* at 85% boiler pressure

nine-coach trains between Norwich and London. Departures
from London were at 30 minutes past the hour, those stopping at
Ipswich only leaving at the odd hour. The 3.30pm down, The
Broadsman, was for a brief period until surpassed by the
Bristolian on the Western Region the fastest train in the kingdom,
covering the 115 miles via Colchester in exactly two hours.

The honour of being entrusted with the first of these new
national standard locomotives was fully appreciated at both
Stratford and Norwich depots, where no efforts were spared to
ensure their success, well knowing that their performance would
be subjected to the closest scrutiny and widely publicised. New
and intensive working diagrams incorporating two round trips
daily to either London or Norwich were introduced at Norwich:

Diagram No	Mileage	Diagram No	Mileage
1	476	5	372
2	246	6	238
3	460	7	372
4	367		

Over a period of ten years the original eight locomotives allocated
to Norwich, Nos 70006–13, accumulated a total of 5,806,919
miles – an average yearly mileage each of 72,586 miles.

Inspired by the example of the LNWR Precedent class
locomotive Charles Dickens, which in the 1890s ran over 1,700,000
miles in seventeen years on the Manchester expresses, it was my
ambition to obtain ¾-million miles from each of my Britannias
within a decade, a target that seemed just possible of attainment,
bearing in mind that two round trips over a shorter distance would
inevitably double the turnround time at terminals. I did not quite
succeed in achieving my ambition, but proved beyond doubt the
locomotives' reliability when worked hard and intensively over a
long period:

Locomotive No	Mileage	Locomotive No	Mileage
70006	737,716	70010	718,686
70007	690,932	70011	675,303
70008	706,852	70012	717,621
70009	661,181	70013	698,458

The Britannias, incorporating in their design some of the best features of regional practice, provided a liberal education in locomotive practice, for it was now possible to compare the design and performance with other companies' products.

Some features such as roller bearings, manganese steel axlebox liners, boilers fitted with monel metal stays and pressed to 250 lb/sq in were entirely new to East Anglia. I was therefore particularly anxious that prior to washing-out with cold water the cooling down of these long high-pressure boilers should be done properly if broken stays and consequent loss of availability were to be avoided.

Norwich motive power depot had a strange mixture of good and bad practices. Some were excellent and these I gladly adopted. Others were frankly barbarous, such as expelling steam and water from a boiler immediately the fire had been withdrawn, and loose shunting the locomotives into the shed and straight away hosing it out with cold water in order to get it back into service as quickly as possible. It is not surprising therefore that the racking stresses set up by this brutal treatment caused stays to break with a report like a pistol shot, thus creating the very condition that the malpractice was intended to avoid. It took long and persistent pressure to eradicate this bad practice, only finally exorcised by the retirement of the boiler foreman. Thereafter when emptying a boiler a constant level of water was maintained in the glass by not allowing hot water to escape from the blow-off cock any faster than cold water could be injected into the barrel. The boiler was not emptied until the temperature of the water was tepid and only then did washing-out with cold water commence. For the Britannias an LMS cooling-down valve for regulating the flow of water was obtained. These measures applied to all classes resulted in a gratifying reduction in the number of broken stays per annum from over 300 to about 30 for a fleet of 120 engines.

I had since 1936 kept a notebook recording particulars of interesting failures, wear of components and data of various kinds not to be found in textbooks or engineers' pocket reference books. The mechanical history of the B1 4–6–0s had been fairly comprehensively documented, and the advent of the Britannias provided a wonderful opportunity to record their case histories in even greater detail. With the announcement of the modernisation plan in 1954 and the sudden realisation that the end of steam was in sight, I decided to record examples of the commonplace as well as the unusual happening in steam locomotive experience, in the belief that the commonplace then would be the rarity of the future.

The performance of the Britannias at Norwich has therefore been recorded in greater detail than any other class and it has to be seen in this perspective as a faithful record of the day-to-day problems involved in maintaining a steam locomotive, and not as a catalogue of its ills. Examining these records in retrospect certain troubles loomed large at the time because they were repetitive. They were in fact confined to one or two locomotives only, like No 70007's propensity for breaking its smokebox cradle bolts or No 70030's addiction to bouts of violent slipping at speed.

Within a month of its arrival at Norwich No 70006 *Robert Burns* was selected to undergo a series of dynamometer car tests on the up and down East Anglican Express, in order to assess the performance of the new locomotives on this service against that of the B1s they were replacing:

4 & 5 June 1951.   Class 7 No 70006.
    8 bogies and dynamometer car
6 & 7 June 1951   Class 7 No. 70006.
    11 bogies and dynamometer car
11 & 12 June 1951.   Class B1 No 61270.
    8 bogies and dynamometer car

A comparison of the two locomotives and their performance when hauling the eighteen trains is summarised below:

Class		7MT	B1
Cylinders		20inx28in	20inx26in
Coupled wheel diameter		6ft 2in	6ft 2in
Boiler pressure (lb/sq in)		250	225
Heating surface total (sq ft)		3,192	2,005
Grate area (sq ft)		42.0	27.9
Tractive effort (lb @ 85% boiler pressure)		32,150	26,878
Locomotive No	70006	61270	
Date	5.6.51	12.6.51	
Distance (miles) –			
Liverpool St–Norwich	115	115	
Timing (mins)	127	127	
Load (tons)	313.5	313.5	
Coal: lb (round trip)	8,453	8,876	

	Up	Down	Up	Down
Coal: lb/mile	36.75	36.75	38.20	38.60
Coal: lb/ton mile	–	0.118	0.112	0.124
Water: consumption (galls)	3,182.50	3,550.00	3,139.00	3,131.00
Water: gal/mile	27.50	30.90	27.30	27.20
Water: lb/drawbar HP hour	23.42	27.70	–	24.55
Water evaporated (lb) per 1 lb of coal (round trip)		7.85		7.08

I rode in the dynamometer car behind No 70006 and noted that 1,000hp was exerted in lifting the train out of the valley of the Orwell on leaving Ipswich and again when climbing Stanway bank south of Colchester, while 800hp sufficed for the long pull to the summit at Ingrave. The working of the locomotives at these peaks was as follows:

Place	Time	Boiler pressure lb/sq in	Steamchest pressure lb/sq in	Regulator	Cut-off %	Drawbar pull tons	Speed mph
Bentley	12.49	235	220	Full	35	3	44
Stanway	13.05	230	220	Full	40	4–4½	30
app Shenfield	13.31	230	210	Full	35	2¼	66

Boiler and steamchest pressures some 10 lb higher than these were usual in later years when firemen had mastered the skill of firing a wide grate.

A high-frequency oscillation of approximately ⅛in persisted throughout the journey. During braking or when the regulator was eased at speed a periodic surging to and fro developed, causing a fluctuation in drawbar pull of approximately one ton. This unpleasant vibration was transmitted to the restaurant car which at that period was near the head of the train, to the extreme discomfort of the diners; stained tablecloths and saucers slopping over became synonymous with haulage by a Class 7MT. This fault was traced to the method of connecting the locomotive and tender with a spring-loaded drawbar, the spring comprising a number of massive reinforced indiarubber pads as used on many LNER locomotives. This arrangement was perfectly satisfactory for a three-cylinder locomotive which to a large extent was self-balancing, but not so good when applied to a powerful two-cylinder locomotive with its greater fluctuation in torque, for there was then a tendency for the locomotive to pull away from its tender at every stroke of its pistons, especially when the reciprocating balance was low. The indiarubber drawbar spring which had been turned out of Crewe works with an initial compression of ⅜in, equivalent to a loading of 15 tons, was examined on the locomotive's return to Norwich and tightened up a further ⅜in to which ¼in was added on the morning of 6 June when the train load was increased to twelve vehicles.

The greater power exerted by the locomotive to haul this heavier load so increased the violent shuttling movement of the tender that on arrival at Ipwich where water had to be taken the firemen was standing ankle-deep in coal shaken onto the footplate, and he had no alternative but to shovel this into the firebox in order to enable the cab door to be opened, thus rendering valueless the coal consumption for that day. Worse still, the violent to-and-fro movement imparted to the dynamometer car had seriously loosened the tyre of its distance measuring wheel. Several anxious hours and much hard work were spent in devising and effecting a satisfactory temporary repair that would see the car through the rest of the tests. Roland Bond, chief officer for design came post-haste from Derby to see for himself what was happening and as a result the type of intermediate drawgear used by the GWR and LMS was substituted. With this arrangement, locomotive and tender were united by a solid drawbar and kept apart by powerful intermediate buffers; the combined weight of locomotive and tender was sufficiently great to damp down and absorb the disturbing forces set up by the former. This method of coupling was adopted by O.V.S. Bulleid for his three-cylinder Pacifics, whereby he was enabled to dispense entirely with reciprocating balance, so achieving the minimum possible hammerblow.

In the early days of the Britannias a slight deviation from the drawings in the manufacture of two minor details caused considerable annoyance to GE drivers – a tendency for injector and brake ejector steam valves to seize in the closed position. The hand wheels lacked the usual projecting spoke that enabled the valve to be knocked open or closed. Consequently resort had to be made to a spanner inserted between the spokes of the handwheel to obtain the necessary leverage; this often slipped and broke the adjacent cab sliding window. This fault was doubly exasperating to drivers accustomed to the Gresham & Craven or Davies & Metcalfe ejectors where a single handle served the dual purpose of applying and releasing the brake, a great convenience if stopping short was likely. On the BR locomotives this was a two-handed job, the right hand applying the application valve while the left was required to open the ejector steam valve.

Investigation revealed that the rounded end of the steam spindle had too large a bearing area in the loose valve attached to it and caused excessive friction. This fault was overcome by partially sinking a $^3/_{16}$in cycle ball bearing into the end of the steam spindle, thus concentrating the load at the point or centre of the spindle where torsional friction is nil. It proved most effective, enabling the steam valve to be opened or closed easily with one hand, yet remaining absolutely steamtight. Torsional friction was also responsible for the nut of the reversing screw jamming in either full forward or full backward gear; a simple stop limiting the travel of the reversing screw did not cure this particular problem.

Ten years' experience with the Britannias on express work in East Anglia demonstrated the extreme reliability and low cost of maintaining the solid cannon type taper roller-bearing axleboxes fitted to them. It should be explained that the solid cannon type box was mounted on the axle before the wheels were pressed on the therefore could not be taken apart for inspection without first removing the wheels. To the best of my belief, all the Norwich Britannias retained their original bearings right to the end with the exception of No 70007 *Coeur de Lion*, which after running $^2/_3$-million miles failed with a split cannon box casting at the RD bearing, caused by a thermal crack where the maganese horn liner had been welded on.

The average amount of oil added weekly to top-up the driving axle bearings of each of the ten locomotives over a period of 48 weeks (including two complete oil changes on account of emulsification) was slightly less than one pint. This was a welcome change indeed from the time-consuming and costly process of refacing the horns and overhauling the plain bearing axleboxes of the B1s every 50,000 miles or so, because of their inadequate bearing surfaces.

It would be wrong to attribute this improvement solely to the roller bearings, as No 70035 *Rudyard Kipling* had all its coupled

ENG N? 70007   8 · 9 · 61

R D TIMKEN _Cannon Axlebox_ (Grease Lubricated)
found broken. Detected by brightness of End Cover
retaining bolts on opposite side where these had been
struck by wheel boss
Cause Fatigue fracture commencing from thermal cracks
along centre line where manganese liners had been
welded to cannon box . N.B Opposite (LH) side liners also
cracked right across weld + extending into box

Mileage since New (May 1951) until 17·6·61 = <u>690,932</u>

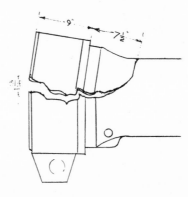

wheels fitted with large conventional type axleboxes lined with
white metal and no difference in riding or performance could be
detected; it does emphasise though, the importance of having
adequate size bearings. Just as in mechanics there can be no action
without a corresponding reaction, so there can be no advantage
without a corresponding disadvantage. In the case of roller
bearings it was the tendency of big-end and coupling rod bushes to
loosen in their rods, often accompanied by heating due to the
oiling rings being forced off and destroying the side play. It was a
common sight when a Britannia came in for its 'X' or shed day to
see on the floor of the machine shop a row of rods and a pile of
bushes metalled-up on the outside waiting to be pressed back in.
At first this abnormality was attributed to the softness of the
bronze of which the bushes were made, but it persisted to a
slightly lesser extent when the repair of the locomotives was
transferred to Doncaster. Thinking over this problem afresh it

may well be that this loosening was caused by the unyielding nature of the roller bearings. Unfortunately I cannot now recall whether or not No 70035 which had plain axleboxes was free from this fault.

Between 1952 and 1954 cracks were found on five locomotives in some piston rod cone ends just inside the crosshead. No 70001 *Lord Hurcombe* broke its left-hand piston rod when at speed on the downhill stretch from Forncett. This must have been discharged from the cylinder like a projectile from a gun, for it was found in the cess where it had rolled, while fragments of the demolished cylinder cover littered the ballast. Had it been the right-hand piston rod that broke when an up train was passing the consequences could well have been calamitous. Piston rods fracturing at the cone end were nothing new, especially when the rods were old and fatigued by repeated flexing, but it was disturbing to find this happening on new locomotives, especially when these were provided with a broad shallow stress relieving groove adjacent to the cone end. The defective rods were renewed and a searching test made of the remainder at every shed day, but the reason for the rods flexing remained obscure until one afternoon the district locomotive inspector reported that the mechanical lubricators of the Britannia on which he had just ridden 'were jumping up and down!'

Naturally I wanted to see this remarkable phenomenon for myself, and hastening to the ashpit where the locomotive was standing instructed the driver to put the tender handbrake hard on, oil the rails underneath the driving wheels and give the locomotive steam. The resulting volcanic eruption as the locomotive slipped violently not only proved beyond doubt that the lubricators did indeed 'jump up and down' but fetched our little man out of his office at the double with sparks flashing from his eyes, a characteristic of his when on the warpath – however, he was suitably mollified when it was demonstrated to him that the reason for the piston rods flexing and breaking had been discovered.

The motion bracket on top of which the lubricators were mounted also carried the slide bars and the whole assembly was rocking up and down like a see-saw because the rivets attaching the bracket to the frame had loosened. Since the crosshead to which the piston rod was connected slid between these bars, this rocking action was causing the rod to flex at every stroke. In order to secure the motion plate more securely to the frame the rivets were replaced by turned bolts and the problem was thought to have been solved until four years later, cracks were again found in the rods of three locomotives. In order to ascertain if the slide bar brackets of other locomotives were loosening a spring-loaded scriber was attached to one of the piston gland studs, its point bearing on the thick brass glut or shim separating the upper from the lower slide bars which on the Britannias were supported independently of the cylinders, after the manner of the Bulleid Pacifics and Lord Nelson class 4–6–0s on the Southern Region.

If indeed the slide bars were rocking up and down the magnitude of this movement would be traced by the scriber in a series of vertical scratches on the brass block. A round trip to London revealed that the pattern of scratches was not confined to a small vertical band as expected but was in the form of a disc about the size of a small pea, clearly indicating that not only were the slide bars rocking up and down slightly, but the frames too were flexing between the cylinders and driving wheels. This was caused no doubt by the increased leverage exerted by the large high-pressure cylinders that overhung the frames to a greater extent than is normal. This increase in overhang was the result of narrowing the distance between the frame plates in order that the fabricated horn checks should project an equal amount on either side, thus relieving the frames of the bending forces that caused the conventional plate frame to flex and ultimately break at the horn gap because the horns projected on one side only. O.V.S. Bulleid initiated this improvement, once described as the nearest approach to a bar frame in British practice. He applied it with success to his three-cylinder Pacifics, but in these the centre cylinder provided a massive and efficient stay between the two outside cylinders, proving yet again that all locomotive design was a matter of compromise.

Once the initial teething troubles described by E. S. Cox in his book *British Railways Standard Steam Locomotives*, notably loosening of the coupled wheels on their axles and the breaking of piston heads through water being carried over into the cylinders in large quantities had been overcome, the Britannias set a new high standard of reliability, some running up to 300,000 miles before their first major works repair.

Hitherto it had been the condition of the boiler that decided when a locomotive was to be shopped but then tyre wear became the limiting factor. This gratifying improvement in boiler performance resulted from a much cleaner internal condition since the introduction of an American anti-foaming compound (polyamide) which enabled feed water to be softened to a new low level of 4° to 6° of hardness without risk of priming. To be able to see the threads on a boiler stay and the copper of which the plates were made came as a revelation to those of us accustomed to sifting a boiler every six months in order to remove sediment and scale.

The years 1952 to 1958 were those during which the Class 7MT 4–6–2s gave their most reliable and trouble-free performance. It was only after six years' intensive use on express work that some of the earlier troubles began to reappear, together with those effects of age and use to which all steam locomotives are subject. My happiest recollections of those years are of those occasions when putting paperwork aside, I made footplate trips to Ipswich, returning on the locomotive of the down Broadman, which more often than not I would fire through to Norwich so that I could see for myself its condition and how it performed. Things that stand out vividly in my memory are firstly the impression of tremendous power accompanied by a high-frequency vibration as if the locomotive was trying to shake itself loose from its train, and secondly an image of the firehole, a purple-red in colour, seen in the night sky immediately after firing.

A phenomenon that I tried in vain to solve was erratic cylinder lubrication. Suddenly for no apparent reason the front cab windows would become spattered with drops of neat oil, and these were also to be seen on top of the glossy boiler barrel on arrival at Norwich. It was obvious that for a few moments the oil was not being atomised but why I never discovered, despite setting up a special rig for testing and adjusting the spring-loaded diaphragm type atomisers.

In consequence the life of piston and valve rings on the Class 7MTs was abnormally low; 10,000 to 12,000 miles was the average, more often than not it was 5,000 to 6,000 miles, and sometimes less. It was frequently observed on opening-up a cylinder that although the bore had a good coating of oil, the surface of the metal underneath was bright and scored, while the rings were tempered a deep violet blue from heat generated by friction. Valve rings were similarly affected, and on several occasions it was found that the exhaust cavities in the steamchest instead of being a dull black had a coating of limewash, clearly indicating heavy priming. Despite the removal of the Melesco steam drier and raising the inlet of the dry pipe in the dome and interposing a perforated baffle plate, priming occurred to a greater or lesser extent throughout the life of the locomotives and was also responsible for a thick deposit of lime in the superheater elements, which had to be frequently renewed on account of distortion or burning out of the torpedo ends which when sawn through revealed a thick deposit of lime similar to that found in the furred-up end of an injector internal delivery pipe.

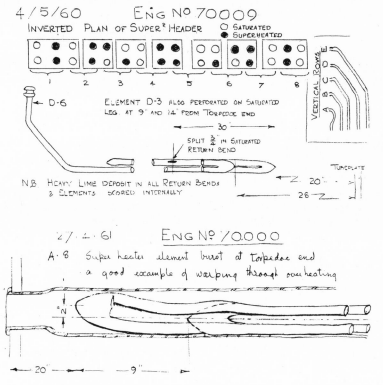

Sketches showing problems with Britannia superheater elements

The year 1958 was notable as far as Norwich is concerned for three reasons. Firstly, the creation of the Traffic Manager's organisation in place of the departmental system, secondly the transfer to Norwich of the mechanical maintenance of all Britannias working in East Anglia and thirdly the introduction into regular main line service of the 2,000hp English Electric diesel-electric locomotives. Railway organisation can be divided into two main types, the departmental and the divisional systems. The former is most suited to the technical departments where a standard practice is essential, while the latter is more suitable for the varying needs of the operating and commercial people where quick decisions have to be taken locally to meet traffic requirements. Henry Worth Thornton had introduced a divisional system based on American practice to the GER prior to the grouping of Britain's railways in 1923, when the departmental system under area managers was restored. In addition to my existing responsibilities on the motive power side, I became responsible for everything at Norwich that either rolled or revolved and its associated staff, the repair and maintenance of carriages and wagons, outdoor plant and machinery and the running maintenance of the road motor delivery vans and lorries.

In 1958 there were still 87 steam locomotives to maintain beside a fleet of 47 railcars (DMUs) and the first of the Brush Type 2 diesel-electric locomotives, and the supervision of 796 men. For this increased responsibility my status was raised to Management Class 2. Gratified at this enlargement of my field of activities, I was more proud of having secured for Norwich the privilege of maintaining mechanically the entire Britannia fleet in East Anglia, an achievement in no way connected with the new organisation. It came about because of increasing difficulty in recruiting skilled mechanics. Stratford had for some months past been sending regularly to Norwich for attention locomotives overdue for major examinations. Those selected were exclusively GER goods types, mostly the big J20 0–6–0s. This in my opinion was a mistake, as the effect of this assistance on the overall condition of Stratford power was negligible. Had the example set by King's Cross been followed, where in a similar predicament some years earlier its A4s were kept in tip-top condition by sending them to Grantham for maintenance, much unnecessary work and heartache could have been avoided.

Meanwhile, Norwich had to continue finding replacements for passenger locomotives that failed on arrival. Often the only one that could be offered was a B1, which evoked from one Stratford driver the comment, 'That'll do me Guv – a Norwich B1 is as good as a Stratford Britannia any day!' This was a nice compliment, but hardly compensation for having to repair yet another 'foreigner' as well as losing one's own locomotive, returned only when in urgent need of washing-out. The allocation to Stratford of the first of the new 2,000hp main line diesel-electric locomotives created yet more maintenance problems for that unfortunate depot, and it was only then that it agreed with an understandable reluctance to its Britannias being maintained at Norwich as from 17 February 1958.

The three-and-a-half years that followed this transfer were the most challenging and exciting of the Britannia decade at Norwich. A condition of the transfer was that there was to be no increase in staff to maintain these thirteen additional locomotives, and this at a time when more and more of the younger men were being trained and transferred to diesel maintenance. Happily for Norwich there was a hard core of dedicated young steam stalwarts who volunteered to see steam out provided that they lost no seniority when eventually they went over to diesel traction. This was agreed and solved the most important part of any staffing problem, its quality. The question of numbers remained, and applying the maintenance unit formula to the thirteen additional Class 7MTs an extra 4½ men would be needed, partly offset by the two previously engaged to repair the Stratford goods engines. It seemed feasible that we could scrape by for staff by doing certain jobs only when they became really necessary, regardless of schedule. The Britannias were scheduled to have an 'X' or shed day every six to eight days, less important classes every twelve to fourteen days, and shunters once a month. Experience with the Class 7MTs had shown that there was no difficulty in running a day or two over the scheduled period, provided that the work done in the shed day, especially the cleaning of tubes and flues, had been done thoroughly. It was therefore decided that an interval of 10 to 12 days between shed days was a practicable target at which to aim, although in doing so there was a distinct element of risk, as an opportunity of effecting a replacement in the event of trouble developing on a Stratford Britannia was remote, since few now came to Norwich after the introduction of diesel-electric traction.

The displaced Britannias were then utilised to provide the Essex coast resorts with a service of fast business trains. A change of locomotives was made on Clacton No 4 diagram, the locomotive of which worked the 9.30am down express to Norwich. If all went well and there were no lengthy repairs the locomotive was cooled down, washed-out during the night, and put back in steam in time to work the 5.45pm up the following day. It was therefore legitimately shown as at work for both days. Ocasionally the locomotive from a later changeover turn could, if repairs were light, be found a job if in steam early enough.

For many years past a serious obstacle to a quick turnround at Norwich had been the lack of softened water in the examination shed where the locomotives were repaired and washed-out. Long delays occurred in shunting them back into the running shed for the boiler to be filled with softened water; consequently by the time that steam had been raised it was then too late for the locomotive to be of any use. Among the surplus equipment sent to Norwich on the closure of the M&GN line was a small diesel engine-driven booster pump from Yarmouth Beach depot. This was put to good use in transferring softened water from the tender into the boiler of the locomotive that had just been washed-out, so that a fire could be lit as soon as it had been shunted into the running shed. While steam was being raised the tender was being refilled slowly with softened water from a hosepipe. This gain in time made all the difference between getting a locomotive back to work on the day that repairs were completed, rather than having it stand over until the following day with an adverse effect on availability. The whereabouts of every Britannia was established by daily consultation with central engine control and arrangements made for those due for examination to be returned to Norwich. This arrangement worked very well on the whole and it was the exception for the interval between shed days to exceed a fortnight. Cases of time lost through priming or blocked tubes were surprisingly few, no doubt due to the regular use of the blowdown valve and tube cleaning lance by other depots, while the effect of long periods in steam was positively beneficial in eliminating those frequent changes of temperature that cause tube and seam leakage.

Despite their partial displacement from the London–Norwich expresses, the Britannias continued to be worked intensively, especially on such trains as the Hook Continental and the North Country boat train. The locomotive of the latter covered no fewer than 576 miles in 24 hours by working first a down freight from Goodmayes to Ipswich, then light engine to Parkeston Quay for the morning boat train to Sheffield, returning three hours later with the North country connection for the night boat, and finally back to London with a goods train to Spitalfields.

High-speed braking tests were carried out between Norwich
and Ipswich on 20 November 1959, with a Britannia on loan from
the Scottish region, No 70053 *Moray Firth*, hauling a 299½-ton
train, including a dynomometer car. A speed of 83mph was
attained at Needham Market up distant signal where the brakes
were applied, bringing the train to rest 35yd beyond the home
signal in 62 seconds on a falling gradient of 1 in 461. Examples of
power exerted were:

MPH	Drawbar HP	Pull (lb)	Place
	375	9,000	Trowse Bank (1 in 84)
40	750	5,000	Milepost 112
50	800	5–6,000	Milepost 111
			185 lb/sq in in steamchest
			Full regulator
			25% cut-off
64	1,000	5,000	220 lb/sq in in steamchest
			Full regulator
			20% cut-off
78	1,100	4½–5,000	Diss
70	1,100	5–5,500	245–240 lb/sq in in steamchest
			Full regulator
			20% cut-off
75	1,100	5,000	Stowmarket
83	1,350	5,000	Needham Market
			220 lb/sq in in steamchest
			25% cut-off

Compared with other Britannias its performance was
disappointing, marred by low boiler pressure in the early stages
and later by sluggish running at speed; it returned north at the
conclusion of the trials.

Just before the outbreak of World War II another Scottish
locomotive was sent to Norwich for trial, No 3401 *Bantam Cock*,
one of a pair of handsome little three-cylinder 2–6–2 mixed-traffic
engines designed by Gresley specifically for service on the West
Highland line, and its performance with 16 bogies surpassed any
other engine that Driver Hardy had handled.

The Britannias, most of which had run ½ million miles, were
now required to run without intermediate attention nearly double
the scheduled interval between shed days. That they did so and
successfully at a time when like any other steam locomotives they

were beginning to show the effects of six years' intensive use is proof of their reliability and the soundness of their design. A statement showing their availability between 1955–1960, the only record surviving, together with another indicating the defects that developed after long and intensive use follows. They fought a valiant rearguard action against the advancing diesels.

Percentage availability of Britannia locomotives

Allocation	10	10	10	10	10	10	22	22	22	22
Year	1955	1956	1956	1957	1957	1958	1958	1959	1959	1960
Week ending	9 Jul	7 Jan	9 Jun	5 Jan	6 Jul	4 Jan	2 Jul	10 Jan	4 Jul	2 Jan
In use	83.3	87.0	73.3	67.0	70.0	72.0	73.0	80.3	72.0	71.2
Under examination or depot repair	16.7	13.0	16.7	28.0	10.0	18.0	8.3	15.2	17.5	15.2
In or awaiting main works repair	–	–	10.0	5.0	20.0	10.0	18.0	4.5	10.5	9.1
Waiting material	–	–	–	–	–	–	–	–	–	4.5

Incidence of defects that developed on Britannias as a result of running ½ million miles on express trains

Year	1952	1953	1954	1955	1956	1957	1958	1959	1960	1961
BOILER										
Fractured firebox seams					3	1	7	1		1
Fractured steel tube plate						5				
Copper wrapper plate bulging						1	3			
Burst and distorted super-heater elements*									40	
ENGINE										
Frame fractures										
behind cylinders						1			4	2
at driving horn						1				3
frame cross stays										1
Wheels shifting on axles		2	1		3	5	7	1		
loose tyres						1			1	1
Slide bar brackets loosening			1			1				1
Piston rods breaking	1	1	3			3				
Drawbar pins breaking					3			2		
Cylinder liners rotating						1			1x2	1x3

*First recorded case No 70003 in July 1952: No records have survived of yearly totals, except 1960

It will be observed that the percentage of locomotives out of service was consistently higher than the depot average for the simple reason that the percentage value of each locomotive was inversely proportional to their total number; in other words one Britannia represents 10 per cent of an allocation of ten locomotives whereas it was only 1 per cent (or slightly less) of the total depot allocation.

Most of the troubles experienced in their later years were those common to all high-powered intensively used locomotives, such as wear and tear of the firebox and frame fractures caused by repeated flexing; these were only to be expected.

Cracks in frames and the rate at which they developed provided a particularly interesting study. While on express work these extended with increasing rapidity but when the locomotive was confined to slow freight work pending its departure to shops, no further extension took place; to use an equine analogy it is the pace that kills!

Inward bulging of the copper firebox wrapper plate at the back corners, about 12in above the grate, was thought to have been caused by the natural tendency of the overlapping plates in a lap joint to straighten out when subjected to an internal pressure, coupled with the fact that due to an unusually wide doorplate flange this area received less support than normal from the adjacent side stays; the distance from the door plate to the first vertical row of stays in the wrapper plate was 7¼in, or more than double the distance (2¾in) between each row.

The early troubles experienced with the coupled wheels working loose on their tubular axles was thought to have been completely overcome after these had been plugged, or solid axles fitted, until late in 1957, when the wheels of No 70013 were found to have twisted slightly on their axles as the result of violent slipping; this was followed at intervals during 1958 by six exactly similar cases.

No 70013 *Oliver Cromwell* was turned out of Doncaster Works on 6 October 1957 after receiving a general repair. On 6 December 1957 the axle keys that located the wheels at a precise right-angle during the pressing-on process were found to be protruding from the leading and driving axles. Axle keys were fitted very carefully before being driven home with a heavy tup – they were then filed flush with the axle end and became invisible when painted. The fact that those on No 70013 protruded 0.20in

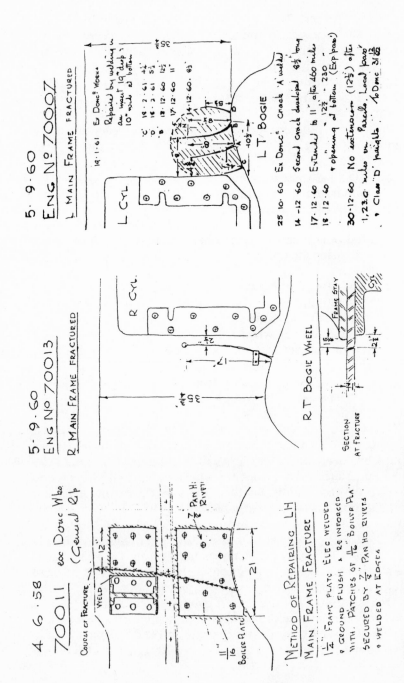

Above and below, Britannia class frame fractures

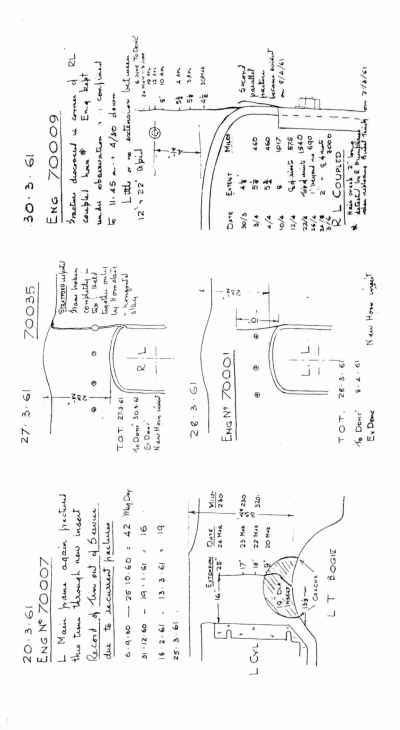

20.3.61
ENG N° 70007

L Main frame again fractured
this time through new insert
Record of time out of service
due to recurrent fractures

6.9.60 — 25.10.60 = 42 Mag Day
31.12.60 — 19.11.61 = 16
18.2.61 . 13.3.61 = 19
25.3.61 .

EXTENSION	DATE	MILE 230
16"	24 MAR	
17"	23 MAR	230
18"	22 MAR	320
9"	20 MAR	

9" DIA INSERT
13½" CRACKS

L CYL
L T BOGIE

27.3.61   70035

STRETCHED w/ptd frame broken
completely in two (left).
Together only by Horn slot
& horizontal stay

R . L
T.O.T. 27.3.61
To Donc' 30.3.61
Ex Donc'
New Horn urgt

28.3.61   ENG N° 70001

.01
3½"

L . L

T.O.T. 28.3.61
To Donc'
Ex Donc 8.4.61
New Horn urgent

30.3.61
ENG 70009

fracture discovered in corner of RL
coupled horn ✱ Eng kept
under observation & continued
to 11.45 a.m. 4/30 down
Little or no extension between
12' & 22' April

6 June to Donc' between
24 May – 3 June
19 Apl
12 Apl
10 Apl
5⅞   4 Apl
5½   3 Apl
4⅞   30 Mar

Second partial
fracture
became evident
on 9/2/61

DATE	EXTENT	MILES
30/3	4⅞	
3/4	5⅝	460
4/4	5½	460
10/4	6	1017
12/4	6¼ inch	575
22/4	7⅝ inch	1940
26/4	1 bought	690
2/5	2"	
3/5		3000

R L COUPLED

✱ Main crack 2" long
detected w/ 2 branching
cracks extending before
finish on 7/3/61

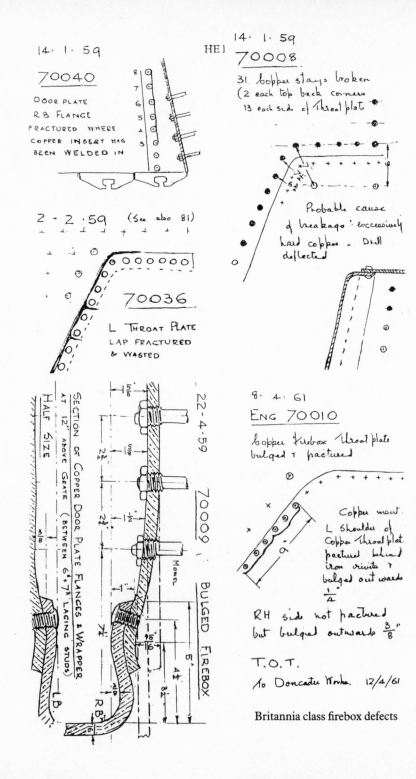

14 · 1 · 59

70040

DOOR PLATE
R B FLANGE
FRACTURED WHERE
COPPER INSERT HAS
BEEN WELDED IN

HE1 14 · 1 · 59

70008

31 copper stays broken
(2 each top back corners
13 each side of Throat plate

Probable cause
of breakage: excessively
hard copper = Drill
deflected

2 - 2 · 59   (See also 81)

70036

L THROAT PLATE
LAP FRACTURED
& WASTED

SECTION OF COPPER DOOR PLATE FLANGES & WRAPPER
AT 12" ABOVE GRATE   (BETWEEN 6" & 7" LACING STUDS)

HALF SIZE

22 - 4 · 59

70009 : BULGED FIREBOX

8 · 4 · 61

ENG 70010

Copper firebox throat plate
bulged & fractured

Copper insert.
L Shoulder of
Copper Throat plate
fractured behind
iron rivets &
bulged outwards
¼"

RH side not fractured
but bulged outwards ⅜"

T.O.T.
to Doncaster Works.   12/4/61

Britannia class firebox defects

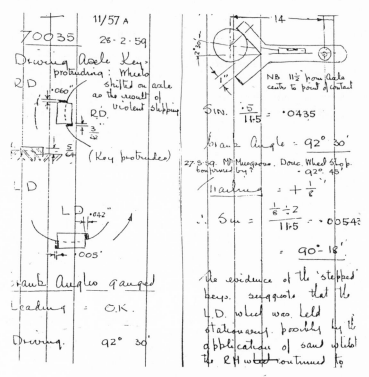

Britannia class No 70035 axle key shifted

and had become slightly stepped clearly indicated that the wheels had twisted on their axles to some extent. The keys having been proved tight, the wheels were replaced under the locomotive and the left-hand coupling rods put on their crank pins, but when an attempt was made to put on the right-hand rods, the leading rod appeared to be ¼in too short and the trailing section ¼in too long. It was obvious that the left- and right-hand crank pins were no longer exactly at right-angles to one another.

The amount of this error was ascertained by setting the crank on one side perfectly horizontal with a spirit level, hanging a plumb line close to the wheel face over the opposite crank when on its top quarter, and measuring the distance between those lines and the periphery of the axle. Instead of being equal as it should be for cranks at 90°, it showed a difference of ¹⁵/₃₂in or half that amount at the crank pin which, with a 14in throw, indicated a crank angle of 89°. Subsequent measurements taken in Doncaster Works with a precision instrument confirmed these rough figures:

Leading – 0.125in obtuse = 90° 14'
Driving – 0.125in acute = 89° 5'
Trailing – 0.025in obtuse

The pressure in tons required to force these wheels off the axle which had a wheel seat 6¾in long and a diameter of 10in was:

	Initital	*6in*	*5in*	*4in*	*3in*
LD	220*	140	125	110	100
RD	270*	150	125	110	100

*These are normal back-pressures; to force on wheels, a load of 10 to 13 tons per inch of diameter was applied.

The wheel seat and bores revealed a good bearing and the wheels were pressed on again after the key ways, which showed signs of shearing, had been dressed up.

In order to avoid the cost of dead haulage, No 70013 ran light to Doncaster as a single driver, as time precluded the realignment of the coupling rod crankpins. I enjoyed the unique experience of riding on this superheated 'single' for part of the way and noted that it ran very sweetly and quietly with a steamchest pressure ranging from 20 lb/sq in to 120 lb/sq in and a cut-off of 25% at speeds varying from 25mph to 35mph. When slipping occurred, which was frequently, the exhaust was barely audible compared with that of a coupled engine, and it was interesting to observe that the position of the driving wheel crank pins relative to those in the leading and trailing wheels generally remained the same due to the effect of the counter-balance weights.

A spectacular example of wheels shifting on their axles occurred on 24 November 1959 when No 70008 *Black Prince* travelling at 80mph slipped violently on a level crossing near Mellis where the rails had been made slippery with mud from the wheels of sugar beet lorries. The slipping was so violent that the left leading side rod buckled, prising off its crankpin cap in the process. The resulting flailing action of the rod, only partially restrained by its connection to the trailing section, caused damage to chairs and sleepers over a distance of two miles before the train was brought to a stop at Diss, where Driver Jones detached his locomotive with the object of putting it into a siding clear of the main line. Unfortunately when doing so the free end of the buckled coupling rod caught in a point frog, bending the rod into the shape of a letter C and under the tyre of the left driving wheel which came to rest standing on its own coupling rod, just as a man might do on his own braces!

During routine testing of piston rod cone ends with flaw detector fluid, three cases of fatigue fractures at the cotterway were detected in 1958. In each instance the crosshead bore in advance of the cotterway was slightly bell-mouthed, a clear indication that the rod was flexing, a not uncommon occurrence with rods that have seen long and hard service.

It is rare indeed for a locomotive to break loose from its tender, leaving it and its train behind but this is precisely what happened to No 70012 *John of Gaunt* when passing Ilford with the 7.30pm down express to Norwich on 9 August 1957. The train, with tender attached, was brought safely to a halt by the automatic application of the vacuum brake. The hoses between locomotive and tender were torn apart. The pressure escaped from the brake cylinder taking all brake power from the locomotive! Driver Shingles, having stopped his locomotive by the time-honoured method of putting it into reverse gear and applying steam to the pistons, was now faced with the urgent problem of saving the firebox containing some two tons of incandescent fuel, with no means of feeding the boiler which was blowing-off hard at the safety valves. He succeeded in saving the firebox by dumping the fire into the hopper ashpan and thence on to the track where it was extinguished by the Ilford fire brigade. The firemen probably owes his life to the design of the Britannia cab footplate that extends right back to the tender front; had it been the usual arrangement with a hinged fall plate between locomotive and tender on which he was standing when the locomotive broke loose he would have been thrown under the tender wheels.

The cause of this mishap was the breaking of the drawbar pin as the result of a fatigue fracture set up by vibration over a long period and the absence of the customary side links or safety chains which were subsequently fitted to all Britannias. Despite thorough annealing of the drawbar and pins whenever locomotive and tender were parted, five more broken pins were found during the course of examination over the next four years.

No 70012 figured in another interesting incident two years later when the left-hand piston valve became disconnected from the combination lever at speed when working the 5.45pm express to London. This accident occurred early in the journey when passing Newton Flotman crossing, about eight miles from Norwich.

9 - 8 57

70012 (D: Shingles)
working 7/30 down
broke away from train at
Ilford — Tender drawbar
pin broken about $\frac{3}{4}$"
from top edge of hole
in drawbar.

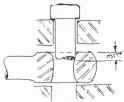

Pin last renewed   ?
"   " annealed   ?
"   " exd in position?

29 · 8 · 57
70007   Bottom portion
of tender draw bar pin
missing (discovered by Beaplin)

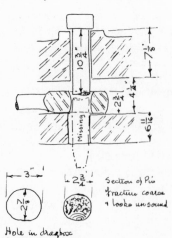

Hole in dragbox
badly worn

25 /10/57

70011 (D: Parfitt) wkg 1/30 Dn
failed when starting from
Witham with R connecting
rod eye fractured + torn
open

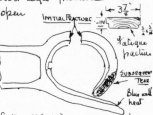

Estimated Mileage since this
engine was built in 1951
   440,000 Kils

Small end last disconnected
on 4th October 57 by fitter
Pawlowski for piston wire
end exam. Given routine
exam on being released off "X"
exam by P. Leeder night of 24th
October

Above. Fractured small end, No
70011
Left upper and lower. Britannia
tender drawbar problems

24·12·59

70039 broke the RH
return crank when passing
Stanway with the 11·30 down

Dr Wm. Parfitt tied up
the eccentric rod and
proceeded to Colchester
on one cylinder, where
a fresh engine was provided
(mins delay)

Engine hauled dead to
Norwich and fitted with an
eccentric rod and return
crank taken from 70040
(Stopped for firebox seams)
cause - a creeping fracture
commencing at the radius
of the return crank pin

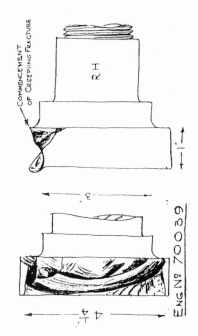

Fractured return crank, 70039

Finding that he was still on the road when the bits had ceased
flying, Driver Sidney Wood kept steam on, and arrived at Ipswich
where a change of locomotives was made.

Subsequent examination revealed that the cause of failure was
the loss of the pin connecting the valve crosshead to the
combination lever. As a result of this disconnection the left-hand
piston valve was driven right forward, permanently closing the
back port and leaving the front one wide open to steam. The effect
of this was to convert the left-hand cylinder into a single-acting
one, with the added disadvantage that every inward stroke of the
piston was opposed by full steamchest pressure. Despite this
handicap, only seven minutes were lost. It was fortunate that the
radius rod buckled under impact with the valve crosshead so
allowing its fork end to ride precariously on the crosshead guide.
Had it not done so, the left-hand valve gear could well have been
completely wrecked and the locomotive rendered a total failure – a

less experienced driver would have stopped to investigate and then found it impossible to restart his train.

Towards the end of 1960 Driver George Ewles reported that No 70013 had suddenly become sluggish and seemed baffled in its exhaust, also that there was a knock coming from the left-hand cylinder. Suspecting a loose piston head, the cylinder cover was removed, when it was discovered that the sleeve or liner that is shrunk into the cylinder barrel, had turned anti-clockwise through an angle of 55°, thereby reducing the area of the steam port by one-third and cutting off the oil supply. Some quick work with a tommy bar inserted in the steam port restored the liner to its correct position before the cylinder had time to cool and contract. No 70005 was similarly afflicted, although to a lesser extent. The cylinder liners on these two locomotives had to be realigned on five occasions before main works could be convinced that merely renewing the locating or grub screw was insufficient to stop rotation.

Several cases of rapid tyre wear due to soft material had occured over the years. Two involved Bissel trucks and tender wheels and were unusual in that the wear was not uniform but was confined to roughly 1ft of the circumference, causing the axles to rotate eccentrically.

During the summer of 1956 engine No 70010 was restricted to freight work on account of a heavy thumping noise that occurred twice in every revolution of the driving wheels, like that produced by the flats on tyres sometimes caused by skidding during braking. However no flats could be found and the matter remained a mystery until one day when the locomotive was being drawn off the drop pit, the bissel truck axleboxes were seen to rise and fall at every revolution of the wheel; when measured, the tyre was found to have worn ¼in eccentric over a length of about a foot. A similar case was experienced in June 1960 when the RT tender spring of 70038 *Robin Hood* was found to be too hot to touch due to the heat produced by friction between the plates caused by the rise and fall of the axlebox as the result of the tyre having worn ⁵⁄₁₆in eccentric – a perfect demonstration of Joule's theory of the interconvertibility of energy.

The summer of 1961 witnessed the swansong of the Britannias in East Anglia, reduced in number to sixteen, but they went out with exhausts beating and colours flying.

When resetting the valves on No 70013 after renewing a scored

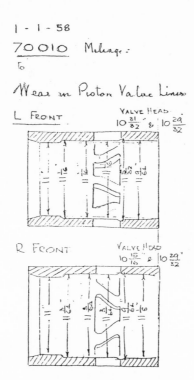

1 - 1 - 58

$\dfrac{70010}{6}$ Mileage :-

Wear in Piston Valve Liners

L FRONT.

YALVE HEAD.
$10\frac{31}{32}$ & $10\frac{29}{32}$

R FRONT

VALVE HEAD
$10\frac{15}{16}$ & $10\frac{29}{32}$

Valve liner badly worn on No 70010

piston valve liner, an opportunity was taken of applying the results of the latest research at Rugby Locomotive Testing Station as to the manner in which the spindles of inside admission valves expanded when subjected to a high superheat. Hitherto it had been customary when making an allowance for expansion (not all authorities, including the French, agree that it was necessary) to assume that a valve spindle expanded uniformly throughout its length. This was probably true in the case of an outside admission valve with heads set close together but not for a modern inside admission locomotive where the valve heads were far apart and the spindle between them subjected to a high degree of superheat. Then the effect of expansion was to move the front valve head forward to a much greater extent in relation to its port than the back. A practical experiment was made to confirm the calculated amount of expansion by passing a length of scrap shafting approximately the same length and diameter as a Class 7MT valve spindle to and fro in the smith's forge, until chips of lead placed in a convenient keyway melted and then measuring the amount by which it had expanded; it was trammelled again when the lead began to solidify as a further precaution in case heating had been local.

A trip on No 70013 after the valve setting had been modified revealed that it was now much more lively and burnt less coal. The nominal capacity of a Class 7MT tender was 7 tons of coal and 4,250 gallons of water, and it was customary before leaving the shed to go under the coal chute in order to replenish that used in building-up the fire. Even so, little more than half a ton remained after two round trips to London (460 or 469 miles according to route), as I know from personal experience in treading the coal down the slope of the tender towards the fireman in the later stages of the journey from Ipswich.

There was on the system a self-weighing tender, but as this was in great demand it was decided to assess the locomotive's performance by measuring instead its consumption of water which could be easily done as the tender was fitted with a well calibrated float gauge. By this time more Britannias had been modified, and a keen rivalry developed between their regular drivers to see who could work the down Broadsman on the least quantity of water, by making it a point of honour not to dip when passing over the water troughs at Ipswich, nor to take water at the station column. Before leaving London the tank was filled brim-full (4,250 gallons) and the level of water showing in the boiler gauge glass marked.

On arrival at Norwich the feed was put on to restore this level before the amount of water remaining in the tank was measured, in order to ensure a reasonably accurate figure for consumption. In the course of these trials that extended over eight weeks covering 39 trips and nine crews, the consumption of water was steadily reduced from around 3,000 gallons to just over 2,500, matched by a corresponding increase in the amount of coal left in the tender on arrival, which averaged about a ton. What had started originally as a scientific experiment had now developed into a contest of skill between the competing crews, and it was to them that credit for this remarkable improvement in economy was due, although the modified valve setting provided the incentive.

By the end of 1961 the diesels had taken over and all steam locomotives had left Norwich with the exception of three departmental B1s, retained solely for overnight steam-heating of coaches, although one was pressed into service on one occasion to cover a diesel failure. I had the honour of firing the last steam engine to leave Norwich, No 5567, a GER superheated six-coupled goods on its final journey, hauling over the western branch lines a Norfolk Railway Society special, organised to mark the occasion. I had much to do with the diesels while I was at Norwich; that, though, is another story.

Had steam survived I should have left it with great reluctance. As it was, I welcomed release from the depressing atmosphere of having to discharge men I had trained, and the sight of once-busy workshops now standing empty and derelict, for now I should be able to spend more time in the world of steam preservation where I had long been active. A letter from the local branch of the Associated Society of Locomotive Engineers and Firemen (ASLEF) and the generous gifts that I received on retirement are prized possessions.

Handing over notes on transfer of 7 MTs to Immingham depot. Autumn, 1961

Summary of experience gained at Norwich between 1951 & 1960 with 10 – 22 Britannia class 7MT locomotives working express passenger trains.

COMMON CAUSES OF FAILURE

Fractured Pipes

1 *Water feed pipe* breaking at flange on Exhaust Injector.
2 *Exhaust Injector Control Steam* pipe breaking at steam chest connection: Also standard is prone to blow out of the steam chest due to stripped thread. (Now to be made of steel and of increased diameter).
3 *Short pipe in front of Drivers window* connecting cylinder cock control steam pipe brake and blower breaking.
4 *Intermediate Steam Brake Flexible pipes* fracturing at soldered collar (less common than formerly). Design improved.
5 *Lubricator Pipes to Steam Chest and cylinders* breaking at swaged cone.

Broken Parts

6 *Mechanical Lubricator spindles*: breaking off and allowing ratchet to drop. Also tubular drive rods where welded and pinned to fork end.

7 *Whistle Cables*: snapping at soldered connections.
8 *Regulator Ratchet springs* breaking and jamming handle generally in closed position: Less common than formerly.

Blows in Smokebox

9 Superheater Header Drain pipe "sandwich" joint on smokebox wrapper; this and the *Blower Steam Pipe flange* joints are the most common causes of non-steaming.
10 *Superheater Elements* bursting at or near the torpedo ends. (40 Elements have been renewed at Norwich on 22 engines since 1st January, 1960).
11 Element joints leaking.

EXCEPTIONAL CAUSES OF FAILURE

12 *Chimney Cowl* breaking and falling down on blast pipe.
13 Air leaks in smokebox caused by *smokebox cradle bolts* continually breaking and falling out.
This has been chronic only in the case of two engines.
14 Draught destroyed by *sheet iron cover over superheater header* rusting through. 70041.
15 *Return Cranks*: 2 cases of fatigue fractures at root of crank pin and one across square fastening.
16 *Valve Spindle Bushes* coming adrift through securing nut working off: Check plates fitted locally has overcome this defect.
17 *Sliding Fire Doors* warping and jamming in slides in closed position.
18 *Tubular Reversing shaft* becoming disconnected at Hardy-Spicer joint – 'Aerotight' nuts or split pins fitted.

Less common but more serious defects that must be kept under continual observation

Boiler

Bulging of copper firebox wrapper plate about 12in above grate at back corners accompanied by bending inwards of door plate flanges: generally to extent of ¾in.

Copper Throat Plate 'Shoulders' cracking through rivet holes or round copper insert frequently accompanied by broken stays adjacent to seam.

Copper Doorplate Flanges: fracturing at rivet holes.

Smokebox Tubeplate: fracturing through grooving at 2 o'clock or 10 o'clock.

Wheels *Loosening on Axles*: A special watch to be kept for protruding axle keys. Nine cases of wheels moving on axles have occurred during the past three years, several resulting in total failures on the Main Line.

Loose Tyres: These rely solely on contraction for their retention there being no retaining ring or rivets. Any sign of slackness especially with thin tyres is suspect.

Piston rods Four cases of piston rods fracturing through the cone end in the crosshead have occurred since May 1958.

Piston rods These are tested for flaws with 'Ardrox' flaw detector when ever the crosshead is removed.

Three cases of Piston Head L.H. check nuts breaking off have occurred. (Later engines have LNE type head forged solid with rod).

Connecting rod Three cases of small end eyes breaking, 'Ardrox' tested for fatigue fractures whenever small end bush is renewed.

Cylinders Three cases have occurred of cylinder liners rotating in the barrel shearing the grub screws and shutting off oil supply and cylinder drain cocks.

Fractured and loose cylinder bolts have occurred on one or two engines.

Frames Four cases have occurred since April 1958 (two recently) of main frames fracturing immediately behind the cylinders where these are cut away to clear the bogie wheels.

The adjacent cross stay between the frames, also cracks at the lower corners.

Bissel truck Welded bosses on main cross stay surrounding pivot pin breaking up (3 cases).

Drawbar pins Five cases of broken drawbar pins have occurred since 9 August 1957, when No 70012 left its tender and train behind near Ilford Station when working the 7.30 down.

All engines are now fitted with safety links.

ITEMS WITH AN ABNORMALLY SHORT LIFE OR GIVING SPECIAL TROUBLE

Piston Rings

Average life 10–12,000 miles. Diminishes rapidly when ring grooves wear taper.

Piston packing

Turning of piston rods due to formation of shoulders at the extremity of the stroke is frequently necessary. (10 rods turned in 24 months).

Side rod and big bushes

The driving side rod bush in particular is prone to work slack in the rod: When this occurs the oiling ring is forced off and side play destroyed with resultant heating.

Issued since stock survey 8.2.60.

Big-end bushes   18
Driving side rod   20

Knuckle pin bushes

Wear excessively and should be renewed when there is 1/16in knock. Rate of wear increases rapidly beyond this limit.

Superheater elements

40 burst elements (principally in the top row) have been renewed since 1.1.60.

Ash hopper gear

Excessive wear on 'dogs' and square, resulting in R.H. door remaining open 2in when 'shut' causing a cascade of hot cinders when running.

INDEX